HeartWarming Sacred Favorites Vol. 2

COMPILED BY: W. Elmo Mercer
James Van Hook
Don Hart
Sarah Long

RISE AGAIN

Words and Music by DALLAS HOLM
Arr. by W. Elmo Mercer

A♭ B♭/A♭ D♭/A♭ A♭ D♭/E♭ E♭
8
A♭ A♭ B♭/A♭
1. Go a - head, Drive the nails in my
D♭/A♭ A♭ D♭/E♭ E♭
hands; Laugh at me where you stand; Go a -
8
A♭ B♭/A♭
head, and say it is - n't me; The

Db/Ab
Ab
Db/Eb
Eb
day will come when you will see! 'Cause I'll
CHORUS:
Ab
Gb/Ab
Db
Fm/C
Bbm7
(1 - 2) rise a - gain; Ain't no pow'r on
(3) come a - gain; Ain't no pow'r on
Eb7
Ab
Db/Eb
Eb
Ab
Gb/Ab
earth can tie me down; Yes, I'll rise a -
earth can keep me back; Yes, I'll come a -
Db
Fm/C Bbm7
Eb7
3rd X to
1
Ab
Db/Eb
Eb
gain; Death can't keep me in the ground! 2. Go a -
gain; Come to take my peo - ple back.

A♭ B♭/A♭ D♭/A♭
head, and mock my_ name; My love_ for you_
A♭ D♭/E♭ E♭ A♭
is still_ the same;_ Go a - head and
B♭/A♭ D♭/A♭ A♭
bur - y me;_ But ver - y soon_ I will_ be free!_
D♭/E♭ E♭ 2 A♭ D♭/E♭ E♭ A♭
'Cause I'll 3. Go a - head and
8

Bb/Ab
Db/Ab
Ab
say I'm dead and gone, But you will see that you were wrong
Db/Eb Eb
Ab
Bb/Ab
Go a-head, try to hide the Son,
8
Db/Ab
Ab
Db/Eb Eb
D.S.
But all will see that I'm the One! 'Cause I'll
8
Ab
rit. e dim.
Bb/Ab
Db/Ab
Ab

LIGHT THE LIGHT

Words and Music by JOHN STALLINGS
Arr. by W. Elmo Mercer

last time to
Bb7
it will drive a-way the dark, Ev-'ry-bod-y do your part and light the
light,
Eb
VERSE (Solo)
Eb
G7/D
G7
A7
light. 1. Some peo-ple look a-round and see the dark-ness ev-'ry-
2. Keep a read-y hand-shake for each per-son that you
Eb
F7
Bb7
where; They say that things are hope-less and they just breathe a lit-tle pray'r. But
meet; There are peo-ple wait-ing now for you and me to greet.
Eb
G7/D
G7
Ab
Eb
there is some-thing that we all can do a-bout the scene;
Let a lit-tle hap-pi-ness just shine a-cross your face;
Eb
Bb7
Eb
Parts
Lis-ten now and I'll tell you what I mean. Light the
We can make this world a bet-ter place.
CODA
Eb
Bb7
Eb
light. Ev-'ry-bod-y do your part and light the light!

SURELY THE PRESENCE OF THE LORD IS IN THIS PLACE

Words and Music by LANNY WOLFE
Arr. by W. Elmo Mercer

REFRAIN
Db Fm Gbmaj 9 Ebm
Sure-ly the pres-ence of the Lord is in this place, I can feel His might-y
Ab7 Db Ebm7/Ab Db Fm
pow-er and His grace; I can hear the brush of an-gel's wings, I see
3rd time to
Gbmaj 9 Ebm Ab7 Ebm Ab7
glo-ry on each face; Sure-ly the pres-ence of the Lord is in this
3rd time to

VERSE
Db Gb/Db Db Gb/Ab Db Bbm(sus) Bbm Ebm7
place!
1. In the midst of His chil-dren the Lord said He would
2. There's a ho - ly hush a-round us as God's glo - ry fills this
Ab7 Db Bbm(sus) Bbm Ebm7 Ab7 Gb7
be; It does-n't take ver-y man-y, it can be just two or three; And I
place; I've touched the hem of His gar-ment, I can al - most see His face; And my
F7 Bbm Ebm7 Ab7(+11) Db D9 Eb9
feel that same sweet Spir-it, that I've felt oft-times be-fore; Sure-ly I can
heart is o-ver-flow-ing with the full - ness of His joy; I know with-out a
Ebm7 Ab7 D. S. twice
say I've been with the Lord.
doubt that I've been with the Lord.
D. S. twice
CODA
Db
place!
CODA

QUEEN OF PARADISE

Words and Music by DOTTIE RAMBO
Arr. by David Huntsinger

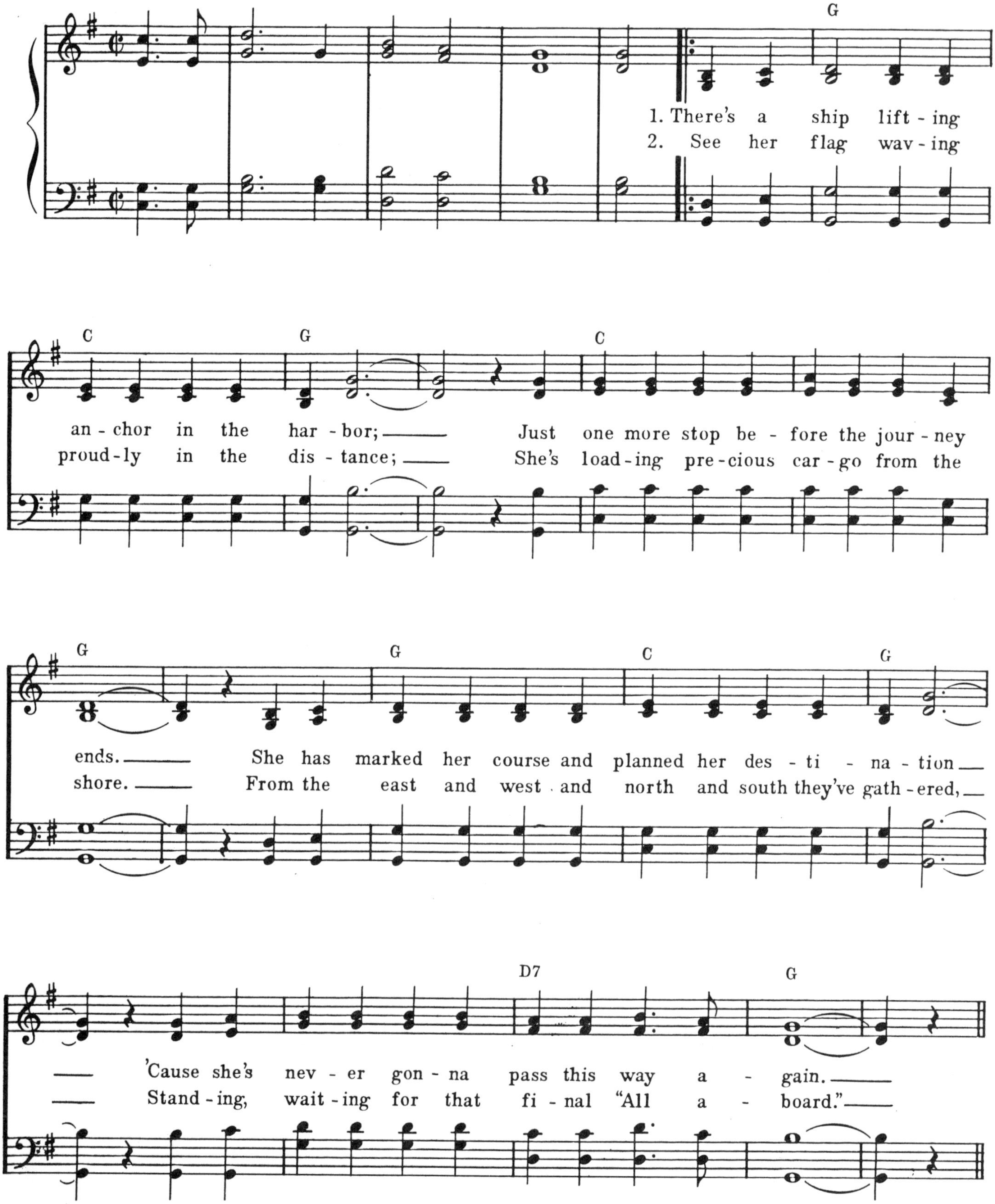
G
1. There's a ship lift - ing
2. See her flag wav - ing
C G C
an - chor in the har - bor; Just one more stop be - fore the jour - ney
proud - ly in the dis - tance; She's load - ing pre - cious car - go from the
G G C G
ends. She has marked her course and planned her des - ti - na - tion
shore. From the east and west and north and south they've gath - ered,
D7 G
'Cause she's nev - er gon - na pass this way a - gain.
Stand - ing, wait - ing for that fi - nal "All a - board."

CHORUS
C G A
She's the "Queen of Par - a - dise"; she's sail - ing by and by, Wait - ing for the
A7 D7 G
Cap - tain's last com - mand. Thou - sands stand - ing on the deck— En - gines
C G C G
full speed a - head, All a - board, All a - board,
C G G/D D7 1 G 2 G
All a - board for glo - ry - land! land!

PEACE IN THE MIDST OF THE STORM

Words and Music by STEPHEN R. ADAMS
Arr. by W. Elmo Mercer

Fm7 C
Bb7
Eb
torn; Tho' I'm wind - swept and
form; In the dark room of my
lorn; Je - sus comes to make my
G7
Ab
Db9
bat - tered I can cling to His cross, And find
suf - f'ring there's a Light comes shin - ing through; He gives me
bed - side a cath - e - dral of hope and love; He sends His
Eb Bb
3
Bb7
Eb
peace in the midst of my storm!
peace in the midst of my storm!
peace right in - to the midst of my storm!
CHORUS
Bb7
Ab C
Bb7 D
Eb
Eb9
Ab
Eb
There is peace in the midst of my storm - tossed

Eb7 Ab Fm7
life; Oh, there's an An - chor, there's a Rock to cast my
Bb7 (sus) Bb7 Eb Eb7 Bbm7 Eb7
faith up - on; Je - sus rides in my ves - sel so I'll
Ab Cm/A C°/A Eb/Bb Gm/Bb Bb7
last time to
broader last time
fear no a - larm; He gives me peace in the midst of my
last time to
Eb
storm!
2. When in
3. When my
CODA
Eb/Bb rit. Bb7 Eb
midst of my storm!
CODA
rit.

THE DAY HE WORE MY CROWN

Words and Music by PHIL JOHNSON

Arr. by Jon Sherberg

Third time to Coda
Fmaj7 Esus4 E7 Am Cmaj7/G Fmaj7 Gsus4 G
I caused all the pain. He gave Him-self the day He wore
mf mp
Third time to Coda
1
C D/E Em D/E Em7 17 G/F Fmaj7 Gsus4 G G7
my crown.
p mp p
2
C F/C C F/C C Dm7 Gsus4 G
my crown. He could have called His Ho-ly Fa-ther and said,
mp mf f ff
Cmaj7 C6 Cmaj9 C6 Dm7
"Take me a-way, please, take me a-way." He could have said, "I'm not
rit. molto rit. D.C. al Coda
Gsus4 G Amadd9 Am/G Fmaj7 Gsus4 G7
guil-ty and I'm not gon-na stay, I'm not gon-na pay."
D.C. al Coda
mp p rit. molto rit.

Coda
Fmaj7
Cmaj7/E C/E
G/D Dm7
my crown.
Coda
p mp p mp p mf
C/G G#°7
33
Am Am(add9) Am
Am/G Am(add9)/G Am/G
I'm the one to blame,
f ff fff
Fmaj7 Esus4 E7 Am Cmaj7/G
I caused all the pain.
He gave Him - self
ff f mf mp
Fmaj7 Gsus4 G Fmaj7
Cmaj7/E C/E
The day He wore my crown.
p mp p
G/D Dm7 Dm7/E G G7 Csus4 C
Fine
mp p pp ppp
rit.
molto rit.

GO YE

Words and Music by REBA RAMBO GARDNER
Arr. by David Huntsinger

Moderately
C
C/B
Am7
C♯o
1. How do we talk to the deaf ears?
(2.) hands are a voice to the deaf ears; His
Dm7
F/G Em/G Dm/G
C
F9/G
What can we show to the blind - ed eyes? Can
words paint a pic - ture for blind eyes to see. The
C
Em7
F
Dm7
we teach the speech - less to sing a song And
heart sings sweet mu - sic our lips can't speak. Lord,

F/G Em/G Dm/G F/G Em/G Dm/G F Em Dm C C7
help all the lame ones to walk in the Light.
fill me with such love the weak lean on me
CHORUS
F Gm7 F7/A Bb Dm7 Eb
He said, "Go, ye, in-to all of the
Bb Ab7 G7 Cm F
world. Teach in that pre-cious name; Sweet love and
8va
Bbo Bb Eb F/Eb D7
grace pro-claim. Not just here and there, but tell it ev - e - ry -

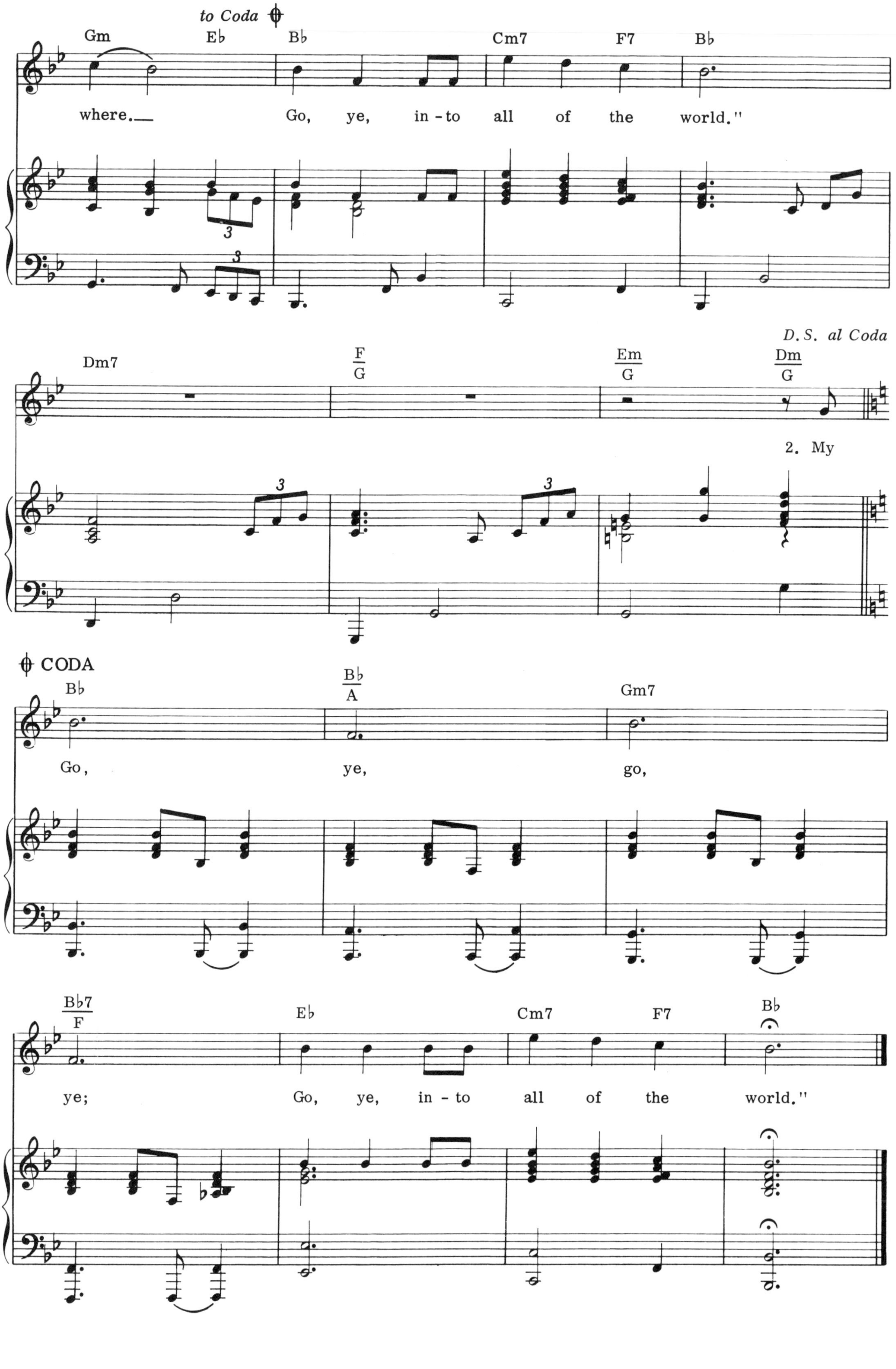
to Coda
Gm Eb Bb Cm7 F7 Bb
where. Go, ye, in - to all of the world."
D.S. al Coda
Dm7 F/G Em/G Dm/G
2. My
CODA
Bb Bb/A Gm7
Go, ye, go,
Bb7/F Eb Cm7 F7 Bb
ye; Go, ye, in - to all of the world."

JESUS, THE SAVIOR DIVINE

Words and Music by TIM SHEPPARD
Arr. by W. Elmo Mercer

9 B♭
B♭/A♭
E♭maj7/G
E♭6/G
E♭maj7/G
Come and be filled with His tender compas - - sion,
He will e - xalt you in kind - ness and mer - - cy,
Though you have wan - dered in sin, He will cleanse you,
E♭m6/G
B♭/F
E♭6/F
B♭/F
E♭6/F
F7
Je - sus, the Sa - vior Di - vine.
E♭/B♭
B♭
A♭add9/C
B♭7/D
Chorus
17 E♭
2. & 3. Won't you come
E♭
F/E♭
E♭
E♭/B♭
B♭
B♭
B♭6
D/F♯
to the wa - ter. Won't you

Gm Gm♯7 Gm7 B♭add9/C C6 C7 Cm7
come to the ri - ver of life.
F7 E♭add9/G F7/A 25 B♭ B♭/A♭
Come to the mouth of the
E♭ E°7 B♭/F E♭6/F F7
foun - tain, Je - sus, the Sa - vior Di -
1,2 E♭/B♭ B♭ E♭/F
vine.
3 E♭ B♭maj7/D Cm7 B♭
vine.
Fine
rit.
Fine

WHAT SINS ARE YOU TALKIN' ABOUT?

Words and Music by HAROLD LANE
and BEN L. SPEER

Db Ab Db6 Ab/Eb Db/Eb Ab/Eb Eb7 Ab
seems I can al - most hear the voice of the Bless - ed Sav - ior say.
can - not re - call what I'm talk - in' a - bout, For His ans - wer is al - ways the same.
CHORUS
Ab Ab7 Db Ab Eb7/Bb Ab/Cb Eb Ab Eb/G Bb7/F
"What sins are you talk - in' a - bout, I don't re - mem - ber them an - y
Eb Ab Ab7 Db Ab
more; From the Book of Life they've all been torn out, I
Eb7/Bb Ab/C Db6 Ab/Eb Eb7 Ab
don't re - mem - ber them an - y more."

HE'S AS CLOSE AS THE MENTION OF HIS NAME

Words and Music by GORDON JENSEN

F Bbmaj7 Am
1. In the ver - y thought of Je - sus, His pres- ence can be
2. ___ In my hour of strug - gle so man - y times I've
Dm Bb Bb/F F Gm/D
found, He's as close as the men - tion of His Name;___
found,
C7 Bb/C C7 F Bbmaj7 Am
___ There is nev - er___ an - y dis - tance___ be - tween my Lord and
Just to breathe_ the Name of Je - sus can turn ev - 'ry - thing a -
Dm Bb C7 Gm7/C C7 F
me,
round,
He's as close as the men - tion of His Name.

CHORUS

Bb/C C7 F Bbmaj7 Am F7 B7
He's as close as the men-tion of His Name,
Bbmaj9 Bb6 F/C C Bb/C C7 F
Je - sus, Je - sus; He's as close as the
Bbmaj7 Am F7 B7 Bbmaj9 Bb6
men-tion of His Name, Je - sus,
Gm7 C7
1. F
D.C. al FINE
2. F Bb F
FINE
Je - sus. sus. (Je - sus!)

HIS NAME LIVES ON

Words and Music by ROGER L. HORNE
Arr. by W. Elmo Mercer

Eo7 Bb/F Cm7 Eb/F F7 Bb Bbo/Db F7/C Dm/F Cm/F
1. There is a
Bb Bb7 Eb F F9 Bb Eb/Bb Bb
name, a name a - bove all oth - ers, A name that's
tried to blot His name from his - to - ry, De - ny - ing
F7 Eb/F Dm/F Cm/F Bb Dm/F Cm/F
stood the end - less test of time; That name has
all the great things He has done; They have cursed His
Bb Bb7 Eb F F9 Bb Eb/Bb Bb
changed the lives of un - told mil - lions, That name is
name, and said there was no Cal - va - ry, But through it

CHORUS:
Je - sus, and this Je - sus is mine!
all, His name still lives on!
His name lives
on, and shall live on for - ev - er, While kings and king - doms
shall all pass a - way; He is the Lord of all, the
King of all cre - a - tion, The name of Je - sus is
liv - ing on to - day! 2. Some men have day!
D.S.

CONSIDER THE LILIES

Words and Music by JOEL HEMPHILL

G G7 C Am
1. Con - sid - er the lil - ies, they don't toil nor spin,
2. May I in - tro - duce you to this Friend of mine,
Am/D D7 C G
And there's not a king with more splen - dor than them;
Who hangs out the stars, tells the sun when to shine;
G G7 C Am
Con - sid - er the spar - rows they don't plant nor sow,
And kiss - es the flow - ers each morn - ing with dew,
Am/D D7 C G/D D7 G
But they're fed by the Mas - ter, who watch - es them grow.
But He's not to bus - y to care a - bout you.

CHORUS

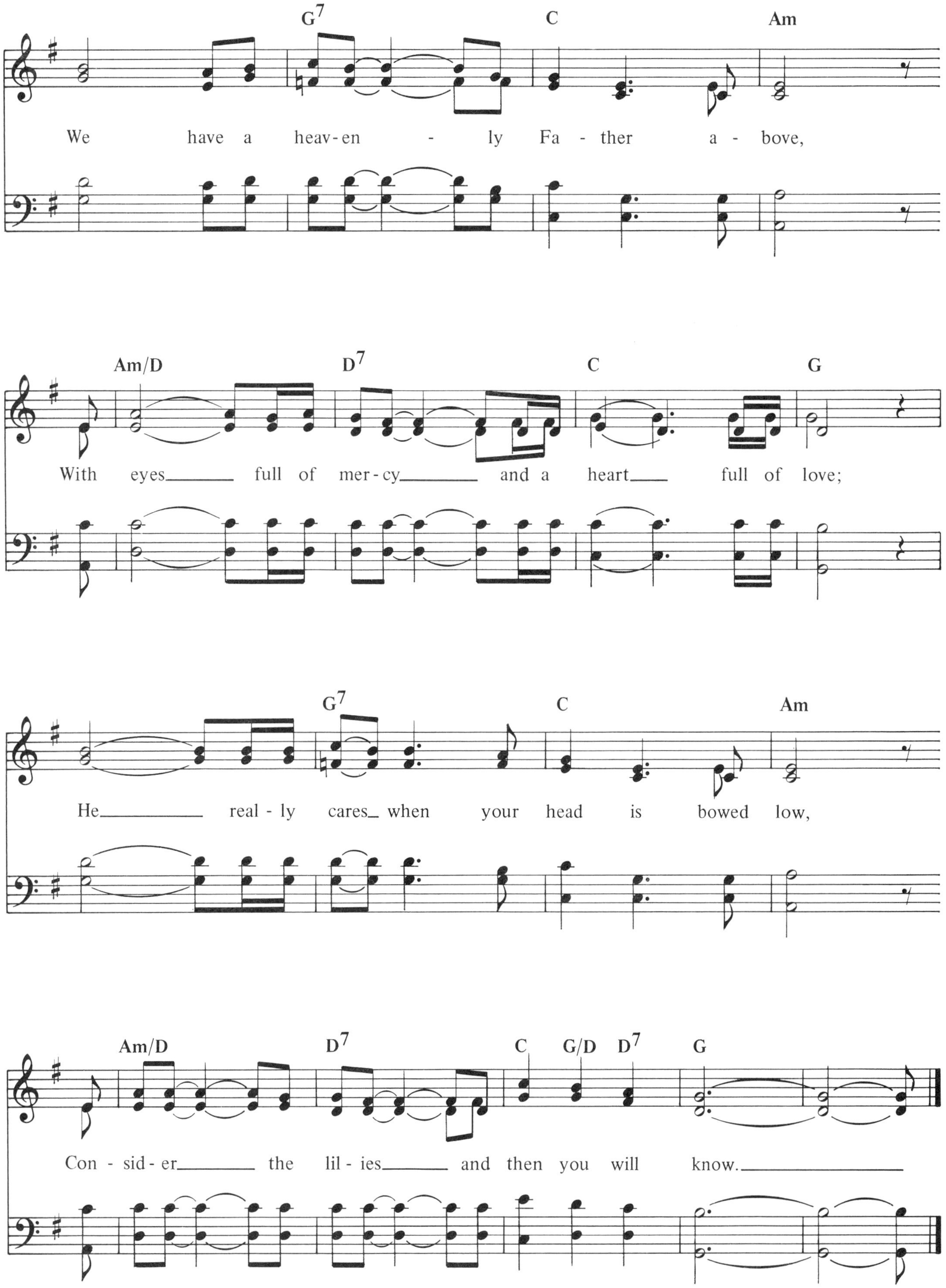
G7 C Am
We have a heav-en - ly Fa - ther a - bove,
Am/D D7 C G
With eyes full of mer-cy and a heart full of love;
G7 C Am
He real-ly cares when your head is bowed low,
Am/D D7 C G/D D7 G
Con - sid-er the lil-ies and then you will know.

WORTHY

Words and Music by RICH COOK
Arr. by W. Elmo Mercer

C7/G Fm Bbm7 Db/Eb Eb7 Ab Cm7 Bm6 (add11)
e'er be heard___ when the saints gath-er 'round God's throne!
all they come;___ Hear them sing - ing re-demp-tion's song!
CODA
BRIDGE
Ab Ebm7 Ab7 Db Dm7 G7+5
more. And I heard the voi-ces of mil-lions, lift-ing mel-o-dies so___
Cm9 Cm Cm maj7 Cm6 Db Fm/Db Bb7
sweet. Sal-va-tion's song they're sing-ing, lay-ing crowns at Je-sus'
Eb7sus Eb7 Cm Bm6 (add11)
REFRAIN
Bbm7 Eb7 Cm7 Fm7 Bbm7 Eb7
feet.___ Wor-thy, wor-thy, wor-thy is the
Ab Ab/C Bm6 (add11) Bbm7 Eb7 Cm7 Fm7 Bbm7 Eb7 Db/Ab Ab
Lamb.___ He's wor-thy, wor-thy, wor-thy is the Lamb!___

PRAISES

Words, Music and Arr. by W. ELMO MERCER

REFRAIN
Gently
G G Am G7/B C
Prais - es, I'll sing prais - es
Am7 D7 Am7 D9 G
to the One who gave His life that I might live;
D7(sus) D7 G G Am7 G7/B C
Prais - es, I'll sing prais - es to
last time to ⊕
Am7 C/D D7 G C/D VERSE
Je - sus, my Re - deem - er, my Friend!
1. He
2. Temp -
last time to ⊕

G C/G G C G/B
sought me out — when I was a sin - ner, — un-done; And He
ta - tion flees — when I speak His pre-cious name, — — Je-sus! I'm a -
D7/A D9 D7 C/G G G9/B C Bm7
told me He loved me — and that I could be - come washed clean, pure and
mazed at such pow - er — and I know that I must be true, and I
Am7 D9 G B7 Em Em7 A7
spot - less — if I would on - ly plunge — 'neath His blood that flowed from
want to; — as long as I have breath — I will tell my world what
Em7 A7 Am7 A♭9
Cal - va - ry.
He can — do.
CODA
G C
rit.
Friend!
CODA
rit.

JUST TO KNOW I'M YOUR CHILD

Words by GLORIA GAITHER

Music by WILLIAM J. GAITHER

G9 Dm7 G13 G9 C Dm/G C
playing no game; So a-
for-giv-en and free. It's
G7 F/G G7 C F/C C7 C9 Dm7 C7/E
ware of my weak-ness, but there's a need deep in-
life's on-ly val-ue when it's all said and
F A7/E Dm7 F/G
side Just to know I'm for-giv
done; There's noth-ing com-pared
G7 F/G G7 C F/C
en, just to know I'm Your child.
to be-ing called Your son.
3

C
G/B
F/A
mf
G13
G7
Dm7
G7
I'm not ask - ing for pleas - ure, sun - ny
Let oth - ers seek rich - es and
3
mf
F/G
G7
C
F/C
C
C/B
Am
days with no rain,
Joy with - out
for - tune and fame
I'd trade all earth's
3
3
loco
8va
G13
Dm7
G7
C
Cmaj7
sor - row, peace with - out pain
treas - ures to be known by Your name.
3
8va
loco
Dm/C
C
mp
C/G
F/A
B
C
Just to stand in Your pres - ence
So that's why I come here
mp
3

C7 F A7/E Dm7
with a heart un - de - filed, And to
to be with You a - lone, Just to
F/G G7 Dm F/G G
know that You love me and have made me Your
call You my Fa - ther, hear You call me Your
1
C C7 F/C C Dm/C C C/G F/A B
child. 2. To be born of Your
2
F C/E Dm7 F/G C
Fine
own.
rit.
p
8va

RISE AND BE HEALED

Words and Music by MILTON BOURGEOIS
Arr. by W. Elmo Mercer

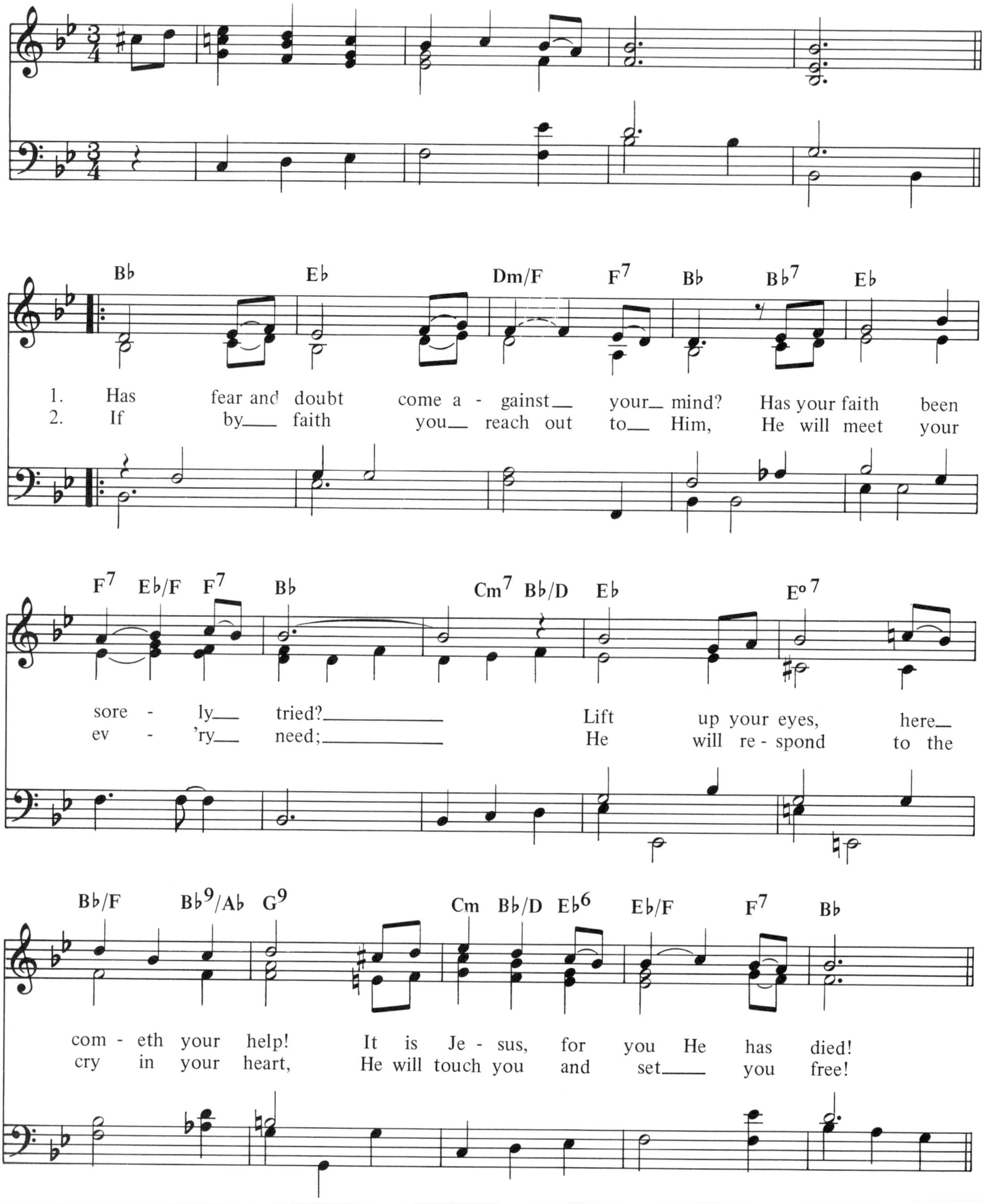
Bb Eb Dm/F F7 Bb Bb7 Eb
1. Has fear and doubt come a - gainst your mind? Has your faith been
2. If by faith you reach out to Him, He will meet your
F7 Eb/F F7 Bb Cm7 Bb/D Eb Eo7
sore - ly tried? Lift up your eyes, here
ev - 'ry need; He will re - spond to the
Bb/F Bb9/Ab G9 Cm Bb/D Eb6 Eb/F F7 Bb
com - eth your help! It is Je - sus, for you He has died!
cry in your heart, He will touch you and set you free!

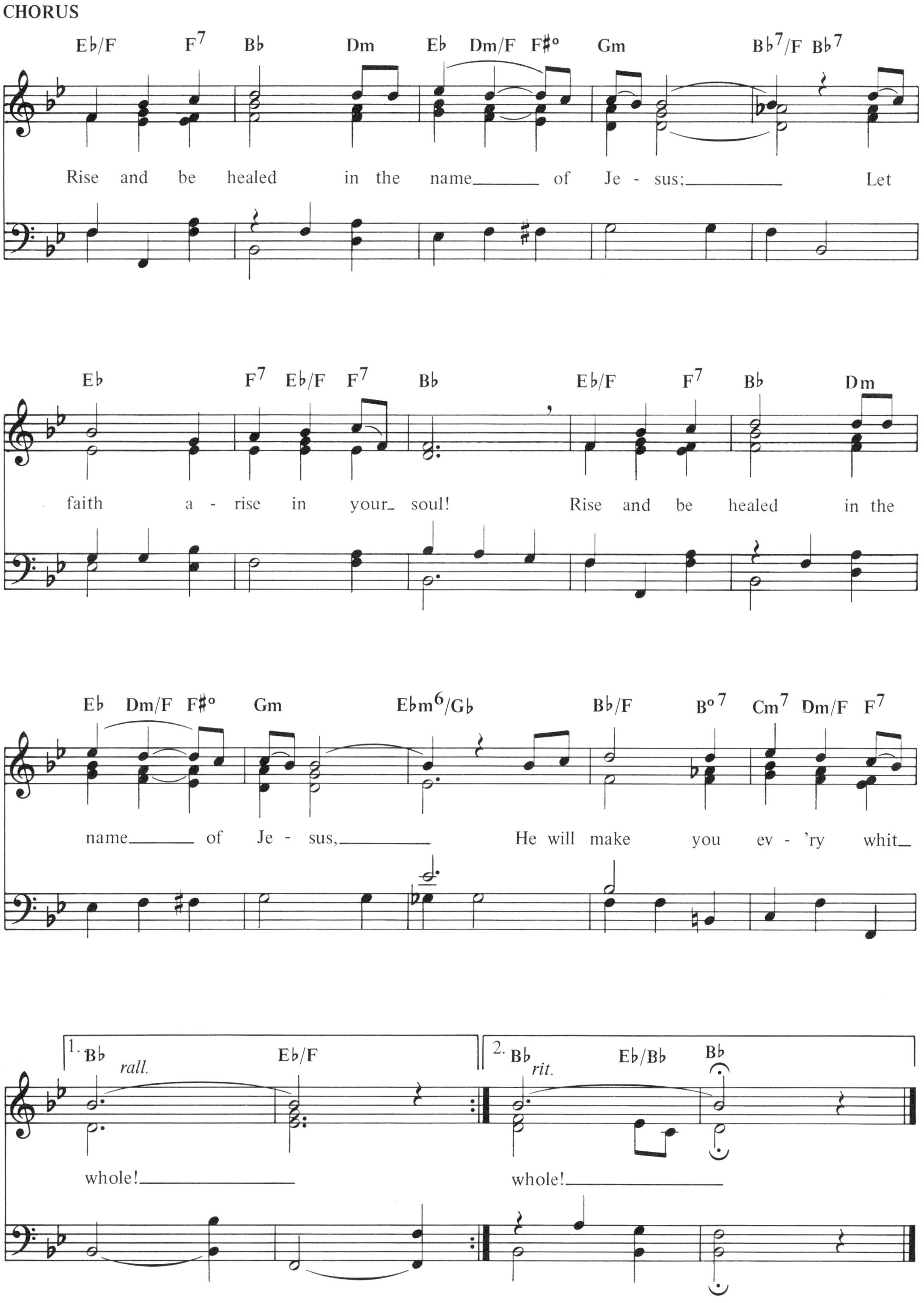
CHORUS
Eb/F F7 Bb Dm Eb Dm/F F#o Gm Bb7/F Bb7
Rise and be healed in the name of Je - sus; Let
Eb F7 Eb/F F7 Bb Eb/F F7 Bb Dm
faith a - rise in your soul! Rise and be healed in the
Eb Dm/F F#o Gm Ebm6/Gb Bb/F Bo7 Cm7 Dm/F F7
name of Je - sus, He will make you ev - 'ry whit
1. Bb Eb/F
rall.
whole!
2. Bb Eb/Bb Bb
rit.
whole!

THE HOLY CITY

Words by F. E. WEATHERLY

Music by STEPHEN ADAMS

Moderately
p
Last night I lay a sleep - ing there came a dream so fair. I
then me-thought my dream was changed, the streets no long - er rang.
p
stood in old Je - ru - sa - lem, be - side the tem - ple there. I heard the chil - dren sing - ing and
Hushed were the glad Ho - san - nas the lit - tle chil - dren sang. The sun grew dark with mys - ter - y, the
ev - er as they sang, Me - thought the voice of an - gels from heav'n in an - swer rang, Me -
morn was cold and chill, As the shad - ow of a cross a - rose up - on a lone - ly hill, As the
mf cresc.
thought the voice of an - gels from heav'n in an - swer
shad - ow of a cross a - rose up - on a lone - ly
f
dim.

rang. Je - ru - sa-lem, Je - ru - sa-lem,
hill. Je - ru - sa-lem, Je - ru - sa-lem,
p
lift up your gates and sing.
hark how the an - gels sing.
Ho - san - na in the
mf
high - est, Ho - san-na to your king!
f
ff a tempo
dim.
1
2
And
And
once a-gain the scene was changed, new earth there seemed to be; I saw the Ho-ly Ci-ty be-

side the tide-less sea. The light of God was on its streets, the gates were o-pen wide. And
C
all who would might en - ter and no one was de -
p
nied. No need of moon or stars by night or
sun to shine by day. It was the new Je -
ru - sa-lem that would not pass a - way. It

was the new Je - ru - sa - lem that would not pass a - way. Je -
grandioso
rall.
ru - sa - lem, Je - ru - sa - lem! Sing for the night is
a tempo
p
cresc.
o'er! Ho - san - na in the high - est, Ho -
mf
f
san - na for - ev - er - more! Ho - san - na in the
high - est, Ho - san - na for - ev - er - more!
f
ff

THE MASTER OF THE SEA

Words and Music by SQUIRE PARSONS, JR.

Not too fast
(TACET) F F7 Bb
1. One night up - on the sea, a ship was toss - ing
2. Tho' the storms of life may rage and the bil - lows
F Bb F
to and fro, Break - ers dashed on ev - 'ry hand,
'round you roll, He can calm life's trou - bled sea
G7 C G7 C (TACET)
an - gry winds a - round did blow; All on board were
as He did in days of old; As up - on life's
F F7 Bb F Bb F
filled with fright as the might - y bil - lows rolled,
sea you sail, trust in Him who nev - er fails.

Dm7 F/C C7 F B♭ F
FINE
Then they called up - on the One who the winds and waves con - trolled.
I'm so glad He sails with me, He's the Mas - ter of the sea.
He's the One who sails with me, He's the Mas - ter of the sea.
CHORUS
(TACET) F F7 B♭ F B♭ F
When He reach-es out His hand, bil-lows cease at His com - mand,
G7 C G7 C
Winds and waves o - bey His will, when He says to them, "Be still!"
(TACET) F F7 B♭ F B♭ F
D.S.
What man is this, they all did say, that the winds and seas o - bey?

ALL I NEED I'VE FOUND IN JESUS

Words and Music by TERRY HARPER
Arr. by W. Elmo Mercer

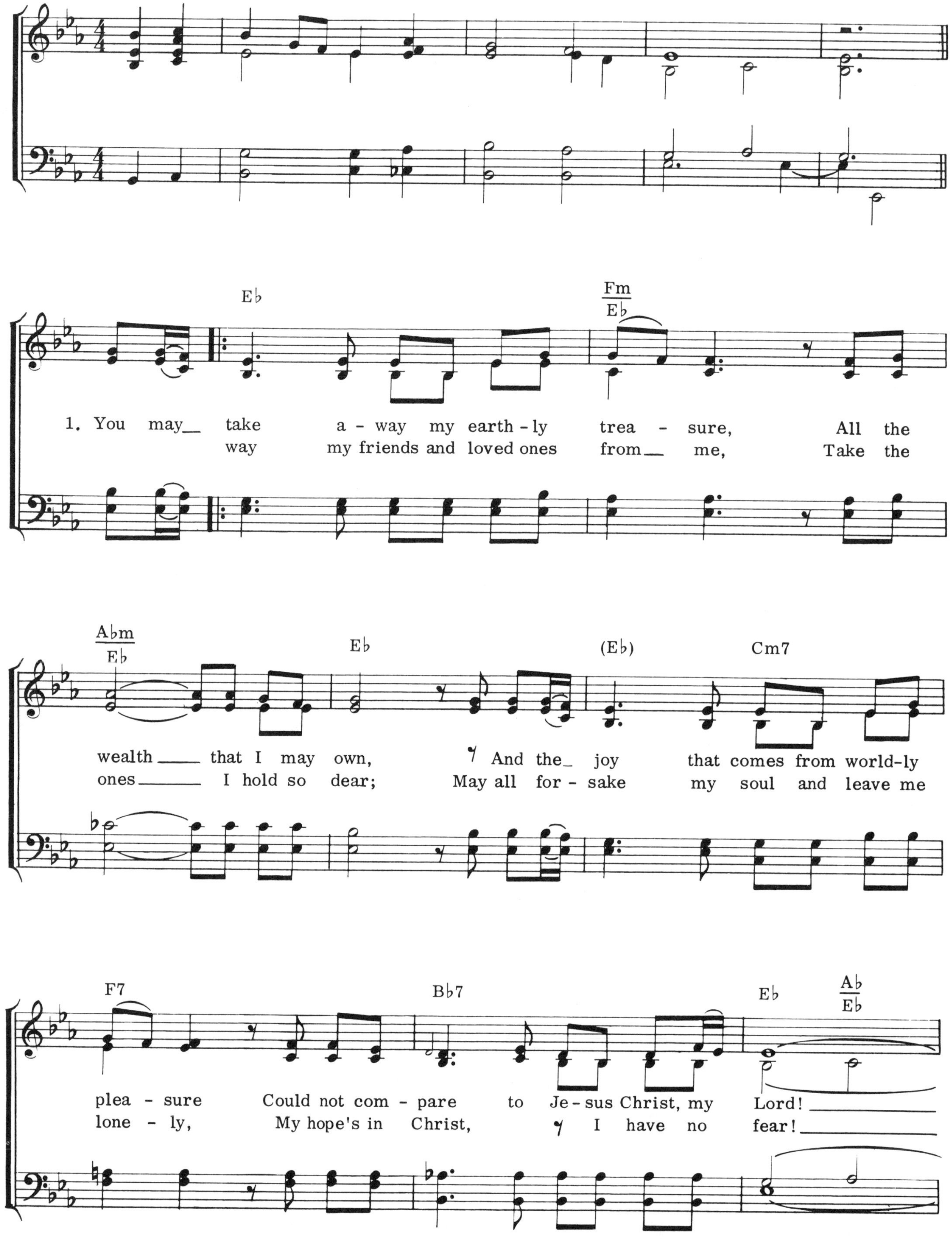
Eb
Fm/Eb
1. You may take a - way my earth - ly trea - sure, All the
way my friends and loved ones from me, Take the
Abm/Eb
Eb
(Eb)
Cm7
wealth that I may own, And the joy that comes from world-ly
ones I hold so dear; May all for - sake my soul and leave me
F7
Bb7
Eb
Ab/Eb
plea - sure Could not com - pare to Je - sus Christ, my Lord!
lone - ly, My hope's in Christ, I have no fear!

Eb CHORUS Fm/Eb Abm/Eb Eb Ab/F Eb/G
All I need I've found in
Ab Eb Eb/Bb Bb7 Eb Eb/D Eb/C C+ C7
Je - sus; He has giv'n me peace with -
F7 F+ Bb7 Abm/Eb Eb Ab/F Eb/G
in; I will praise His name for -
Ab Eb Eb/G Ab Eb/Bb Cm Abm/Cb Eb/Bb Bb7(sus) Bb7
ev - er, For His blood has washed a - way my
1 Eb rall. Ab/Eb Eb
sin! 2. Take a -
2 Eb Eb/Ab Eb
sin!

CORNERSTONE

Words and Music by LARI GOSS

Arranged by W. Elmo Mercer

Ab/Eb
1
Eb7(sus)
Eb7
2
Eb7
Eo7
is the Corn-er - stone. When I
is the Corn-er - stone.
F
Bb/F
F
Bb/F
mp
B
F
Fmaj7
F7
Bb/F
F
C/E
Rock of A - ges, cleft for me,
Cm/Eb
Bb/D
Bbm6/Db
F/C
Dm6/B♮
Bb/C
C7
Let me hide my - self in

C
F
A7+ more intense
Dm
Thee. Rock of A - ges, so se -
more intense
G7
C
G6/B
Am
cure, for all time it shall en - dure; 'Til His
Dm
G7
C
F
chil - dren reach their home He re - mains the
D
E7(sus)
E7
D/E louder
A
C♯m7/G♯
Corn - er - stone; 'Til the break - ing of the
louder

F♯m F♯m7 Bm7(sus) E7 A C♯m7/G♯
dawn, 'Til all foot - steps cease to roam, Ev - er
F♯m F♯m/E B/D♯ B7 E C♯o7/E♯
let this truth be known, Je - sus is the Corn - er -
F♯m F♯m/E♮ Do7/D♯ A/E F♯m
stone, Je - sus is the
Bm7 D/E A G/A D/A A
Corn - er - stone.
3

CHERISH THAT NAME

Words and Music by LANNY WOLFE
Arr. by W. Elmo Mercer

Cm G7/C Cm7 F7 Bb7(sus)
You shall bring forth a Son and call His name Je - sus."
come be-fore Him and a-dore that love-ly name of Je - sus.
mag-ni-fy Him loud and strong, that won-drous name of Je - sus.
Chorus
Bb7(b9) Eb Gm/Eb Eb7 Abmaj9 Ab6 C7/G
Cher - ish that beau - ti-ful name,
Fm C+/F Fm7 Bb9 Eb(add 9) Eb Eb Gm/E Eb7
Cher - ish that won - der-ful name, Cher - ish that
Abmaj9 Fm Bb7 Ab/Bb Bb7 Abm6/Eb
match - less name, That name is Je -

E♭
E♭ Gm/E♭ E♭7
A♭maj9
3
A♭6 C7/G
sus. Cher - ish that beau - ti - ful name,
Fm C+/F Fm7
B♭9
E♭(add 9) E♭
E♭ Gm/E♭ E♭7
Cher - ish that won - der-ful name, Cher - ish that
A♭maj9
Fm
B♭7 A♭/B♭ B♭7
A♭m6/B♭
match - less name, That name is Je -
1-2
E♭
D.S.
3
E♭
sus. (2.) – sus.
3. No

HOLY SPIRIT, THOU ART WELCOME

Words by DOTTIE RAMBO

Music by DOTTIE RAMBO
and DAVID HUNTSINGER
Arranged by W. Elmo Mercer

1. Ho-ly Spir-it, Thou art wel - come in this place; Ho-ly Spir-it, Thou art
2. Ho-ly Spir-it, Thou art wel - come in this place; Ho-ly Spir-it, Thou art
wel - come in this place; Om-nip-o-tent Fa-ther of mer-cy and
wel - come in this place; Om-nip-o-tent Fa-ther of mer-cy and
grace! Thou art wel - come in this place. Lord, in Thy pres-ence there's
grace! Thou art wel - come in this place. Fill all the hun-gry and
heal-ing di-vine; No oth-er pow-er can save, Lord, but Thine; Ho-ly
emp-ty with-in; Re-store us, oh Fa-ther, re-vive us a - gain; Ho-ly
Spir-it, Thou art wel - come in this place; Thou art wel - come in this place.
Spir-it, Thou art wel - come in this place; Thou art wel - come in this place.

PRAISE BE TO JESUS

Words by GLORIA GAITHER

Music by WILLIAM J. GAITHER

F F7 B♭ B♭/F F
1. Let him who is thirst - y come to clear wa - ter, Let
2. The hills and the moun - tains break forth in - to sing - ing, The
3. Then shall the light break forth in - to morn - ing, Bring - ing
F C7
him who is hun - gry come by and eat; For
tall state - ly trees and fields clap their hands; In
beau - ty for ash - es, strength for the days; And
F F7 B♭ B♭/F F
mon - ey can't buy this cool liv - ing wa - ter, Or this
place of the thorn there shall grow a tall fir tree, A
hearts that were heav - y shall stand in His pres - ence,
C7 F
milk and hon - ey so sweet.
ten - der plant sprouts from the sand.
Wrapped in the gar - ment of praise.

F F7 Bb Bb/F F
Praise be to Je - sus, the sweet rose of Sha - ron,
C7
Praise to the Christ, the Re - deem - er of men;
F F7 Bb Bb/F F
Praise to the King who is reign - ing for - ev - er, The
Bb F F/C C7 F
Hope of the a - ges, my Mas - ter and Friend.

I FEEL SO GOOD ABOUT IT

Words and Music by DAVE REDMAN

Ebm7 Ab7 Db
A - bout the things we Chris - tians do and say;
You've been set free so sing this hap - py song;
Gb Ab7 Db Bbm7
But when He gives new life and sets the mu - sic ring - in', You just
Ev - 'ry day I walk with Him He gets much sweet - er, I'm so
Ebm7 Ab7 Db
1. 2.
D.S.
got to tell the world you found the way. If you
glad that in His fam - 'ly I be - long. Oh I
Ebm Ab7 Fm7
CODA
feel so good a - bout it I'm gon - na sing and I'm gon - na shout
Bbm Ebm Ab7 Gb Db
it; I feel so good a - bout it, I've been saved.

I'VE GOT A RESERVATION

Words and Music by SQUIRE PARSONS, JR.

CHORUS

Ab
Eb
I've got a res-er-va-tion to walk on the streets of gold,
Ab
Eb
Bb
I've got a res-er-va-tion where the pearl-y gates un-fold.
Eb
Ab
In heav-en my name's been writ-ten down, I'm long-ing to hear that trum-pet sound,
Ab
Eb
Bb
Bb7
Eb
I've got a res-er-va-tion, my name's been writ-ten down.

IF WE WERE ONE

Arranged by W. Elmo Mercer

Words and Music by PAUL DOWNING
and DONY McGUIRE

Bb/F
Gm/E♮
pen im - mor - tal words, Words that say im - por -
self - ish things at all, But rath - er hopes for oth -
F(sus)
F7
Cm7
tant things, no one has ev - er heard, Then may - be I could feel
er folks are dreams that I re - call; For my pur - pose here is
F7
Cm7
F7
that to some - one I had giv - en, And the
not to see how great I can be - come, It's of
1st vs.
to Chorus
Cm7
F7
Bb
life I've lived would not have been in vain! If we were one
1st vs.
to Chorus

2nd vs.
Cm7
F7
Cm7
F7
shar - ing, it's of car - ing that we all could be as
2nd vs.
B♭
CHORUS
Cm7
F7
one. If we were one this world would feel a peace we've
B♭
D
D/C
nev - er felt be-fore; If we were one we could give love to oth - ers
Gm
B♭/F
E♭
F/E♭
nev - er shown be-fore; If we were one mis-un - der-stand-

Dm7 Gm Cm7 F7
ings would be— gone;— And if the Lord will help— me,— So that
Cm7 F7 Cm7 F7
2nd time to ⊕
ev-'ry-one— could see,— By be-in' one,— if we're on-ly one, What a
2nd time to ⊕
Cm7 F7 B♭(sus) B♭ B♭(sus) B♭
great world this would be!
2. The
⊕ CODA
Cm7 F7 B♭ Dm7 E♭ F7 B♭
rit.
great world this would be!
⊕ CODA
rit.

I GO TO THE ROCK

Words and Music by DOTTIE RAMBO

With a feel
F D7 G7 C7 F F7 Bb/F
F F F7 Bb
1. Where do I go when there's no one else to
(2. Where do I) hide 'til the storms have all passed
F (F°) C7
turn to? Who do I talk to when
o - ver? Where do I run to when the
Bb F F7 Bb
no one wants to lis - ten? Who do I lean on
winds of sor - row threat - en? Is there a ref - uge

F A7/E Dm F7/C
when there's no foun - da - tion sta - ble? I go to the
in the time of trib - u - la - tion? When my
Gm7 C7 Bb/C F F7 Bb/F
Rock I know that's a - ble, I go to the Rock.
soul needs con - so - la - tion, I go to the Rock.
CHORUS
F C7
I go to the Rock of my sal - va - tion, Go to the
Bb F Dm C
Stone that the build - er re - ject - ed, Run to the Moun - tain and the

B♭ G7/B♮ Csus C
Moun - tain stands by me. The earth all a -
F C7/G F/A F A7
round me is sink - ing sand On Christ, the Sol - id Rock, I
Dm B♭ F D7 G7 C7
stand. When I need a shel - ter, when I need a friend, I go to the
1 F F7 B♭/F F
Rock. 2. Where do I
2 F F7 B♭/F F
Rock.

COME UNTO JESUS

Words and Music by DALLAS HOLM
Arr. by W. Elmo Mercer

C G C/D G
can't for - give;
But He'll for - give and for -
Am Am7 D7 C/D D7 G C/D
(Repeat Chorus)
get, my friend,
And show you how to live.
CODA
G E
way!
VERSE
A Bm Bm7
2. Don't you put it off my friend;
E7 D A D/E A
You can't af - ford to wait;
To - day's the

Bm Bm7 E7 D/E E7 A D/E
day for you, Soon it could be too late!
CHORUS:
A Bm Bm7 E7
Come un - to Je - sus, Give Him your
D A (A) Bm Bm7/F♯
life to - day; Come un - to Je - sus,
E7 D/E E7 A D/E A
rit. 2nd time
D. S.
Let Him have His way! way!
rit. 2nd time

BORN AGAIN

Words and Music by ANDREW CULVERWELL
Arr. by Dwight Elrich

Chorus F
Fmaj7
F7
B♭
Gm
25
C7
Born a-gain, there's real-ly been a change in me, born a-gain,
29
F
Fmaj7
F7
just like Je-sus said. Born a-gain, and all be-cause of
33
Gm7
B♭/C
C7
1
D.S.
Cal-va-ry. I'm glad, so glad, that I've been born a-gain.
2
F (tacet)
CHORUS
39
G
Gmaj7
F/G
G7
C
gain. Born a-gain, there's real-ly been a change in me,

43
Am
D7
G
born a-gain, just like Je-sus said.
Ped. (steel guitar effect)
47
Gmaj7
F/G
Dm/A
G7
C
51
Am
Born a-gain, and all be-cause of Cal-va-ry.
I'm glad, so glad, that
3
C/D
D7
G
Freely
f
55
A7
I've been born a-gain.
I'm glad, so glad, that
Freely
mf
C/D
Bm/D
a tempo
G
C
G
I've been born a-gain.
loco
8va
Solo
f a tempo
rit.
8va
Ped.
loco

THANK YOU, JESUS

Words and Music by LADONNA GATLIN JOHNSON

Arr. by W. Elmo Mercer

F Cm/G A♭6 F7/A♮ B♭ E♭ A♭/E♭ E♭ A♭/B♭
E♭ Fm/E♭ Gm/E♭ Fm/E♭
1. I just came to tell ya that I love you;
2. He just came to tell me that He loves me;
E♭ Fm/E♭ D♭ B♭7(sus) B♭7
I just came to tell ya that I care;
He just came to tell me that He cares;
Fm B♭7 Fm B♭7
I just came to pray, to share a lit-tle smile to-day,
He's with me to-day, and I'm a-gon-na let Him stay, So

Fm Cm/G Ab6 F7/A♮ B♭ E♭ A♭/E♭ E♭
I just_ came to_ say, "Thank You, Je - sus."_ And } when all_
I just_ came to_ say, "Thank You, Je - sus."_ Now }
B♭m7 C7 Fm C+/F
_ the world's a - gainst_ me,_ and I'm up a - gainst the wall,_
Fm7 D♭9
_ Lord, You come and give_ me pow - er_ to make a
last time to ⊕
E♭ B♭m6/D♭ C7 Fm Cm/G A♭6 F7/A♮ B♭
stand and not_ to fall;_ (So) I just_ came to_ say, "Thank_ You, Je -
last time to ⊕

1
D.S.
2
Eb
Ab
Eb
Eb
Ab
Bb
Eb
Ab
Eb
Eb
- sus." - sus." Now when all
CODA
Bb
Fm
Cm
G
Ab6
F7
A♮
Bb
Fm
Cm
G
Ab6
F7
A♮
say, "Share a smile to - day;" I just came to
Fm
Bb
Bb
Eb
Fm
Eb
Gm
Eb
Fm
Eb
say, "Thank You, Je - sus, Thank You, Je -
Eb
Fm
Eb
Gm
Eb
rit.
Fm
Eb
Eb
Eb 6
9
- sus, Thank You, Je - sus!"
rit.
l.h.

THERE'S SOMETHING THAT'S DIFFERENT ABOUT HIM

Words and Music by LANNY WOLFE
Arranged by W. Elmo Mercer

(*) 2nd time vocal out; begin narration

(**) 3rd time vocal resumes softly behind narration

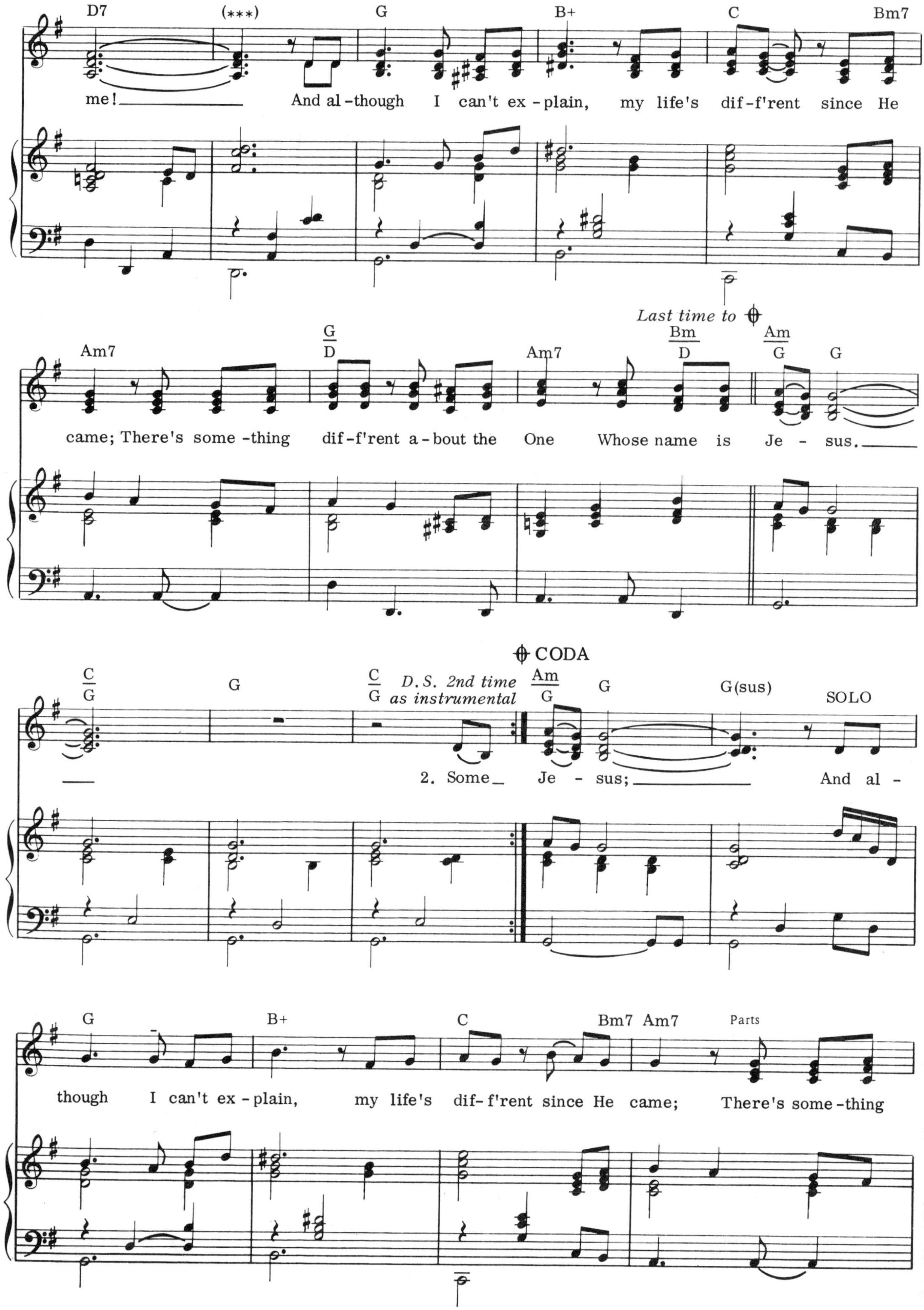
D7 (***) G B+ C Bm7
me! And al-though I can't ex-plain, my life's dif-f'rent since He
Last time to 𝄌
Am7 G/D Am7 Bm/D Am/G G
came; There's some-thing dif-f'rent a-bout the One Whose name is Je - sus.
𝄌 CODA
C/G G C/G
D.S. 2nd time as instrumental
Am/G G G(sus) SOLO
2. Some Je - sus; And al -
G B+ C Bm7 Am7 Parts
though I can't ex-plain, my life's dif-f'rent since He came; There's some-thing

(***) 3rd time end narration; vocal louder to Fine.

G/D Am7 Bm/D Em Em/D Cm7
dif-f'rent a-bout the One Whose name is Je - sus, There's some-thing
rit.
G/D Am7 Bm/D Am/G G
Fine
dif-f'rent a - bout the One Whose name is Je - sus.
rit.

NARRATION:

It was just another day...up that same road...to the same hillside...
Just three more criminals to be crucified...just another day.
Many of the spectators had been there before...just three more crosses...
Three more men...one more spectacle to entertain the crowd.

But, there was something different about this crucifixion...
The sky blackened in anguish to see the Creator of the Universe
Suspended between earth and heaven, as though rejected by both.
The earth shuddered in remorse as it received His life's blood
And the clouds wept bitter tears as if to wash away the scene entirely.
Then all of nature stood in awe as the gray finality of His sentence
Became a fact.

In days past, He walked with the people; He healed their sick;
He raised their dead;
He fed them by the thousands just by multiplying that young boy's lunch;
Why, He even walked on the water!
They saw all of the miracles; but, somehow, they never really saw Him.

His followers had proclaimed Him to be King--King of the Jews.
Where were they now? Where were they now? Had any king ever died such a death?

He had called Himself the Son of Man.
If He were just a man, who rolled the stone away? Why was His tomb empty?
How did He resurrect on the third day? And how did He ascend into heaven?

He wasn't just a man. There was something different about Him.
I know. Not just because history recorded these events.
I know... I know because Jesus Christ transformed my life!

WE DO NOT DIE

Words and Music by SHIRLEY CANTRELL

Ab
Eb7
1. Death is an ap - point - ment that we
2. It hurt us so to watch Ma - ma go, to be gone for -
Ebo Eb7
Bbm
Eb7
all must keep, But as a child of God, we just close our eyes
ev - er - more, But, be - fore she closed her eyes in death,
Ab
and sim - ply fall a - sleep; To be car - ried a -
she heard a knock up - on her door. We o - pened
Ab/C Eb/Bb Ab
Db
way on an - gel wings, up to heav - en's shore, Where we will
wide the door for her and, though we could not see, She said, "A

Bbm Eb/Bb Bbm Eb7 Bbm Eb7 Db/Ab Ab
move right in - to a man-sion, there to live_ for - ev - er - more._
band of an - gels just walked in___ to car-ry me home to glo - ry."
CHORUS
Ab Eb7 Ab Eb7
Grave where is your vic - to - ry?_ Death, where is your sting?
Bbm Eb7 Ab
We do not die,_ we just move on high_ to live with Christ, the King;_
Ab Ab/C Eb/Bb Ab Db
To walk on gold, to see the sights un - told, and with the saints of old to sing,
Bbm Eb/Bb Bbm Eb7 Bbm Eb7 Ab
Grave, where is your vic - to - ry?_ Death where is your sting?

Stand Still and See His Glory

Words and Music by DOTTIE RAMBO
Arranged by David Huntsinger

Intro.
1. Stand still and see His glo - ry; Watch as His mys - t'ries un - fold. Bask in the sweet - ness of pure Liv - ing Wa - ters, Re - fresh - ing, re - viv - ing the soul.
2. All hail His in - fin - ite wis - dom! None is so might - y as He. Mas - ter, Cre - a - tor of all things en - dur - ing, None else is so pre - cious to me.
CHORUS
Stand still and see His glo -

ry. Hal - le - lu - jah! 'Tis won - drous, His vic - t'ries and
tri - umphs. Stand still, ye peo - ple, Be si - lent and
see His glo - ry, Hal - le - lu - jah! His glo - ry, Hal - le -
lu - jah! Stand still and see His glo - ry.
1.
2.
glo - ry. A - men.

I'M STANDING ON THE SOLID ROCK

Words, Music and Arr. by HAROLD LANE

F F7 B♭
1. Thru my dis - ap - point- ments, strife and dis - con - tent - ment, I
2. E - ven tho' He's gone now, I don't feel a - lone now, with
3. Now I'm press - ing on - ward, Each step leads me home-ward, I'm
F C♯o G7 C G7 C7
cast my ev - 'ry care on the Lord; No
com - fort came the Spir - it of the Lord; Now
trust - ing in my Sav - ior day by day; And
F F7 B♭
mat - ter what ob - ses - sion, pain or deep de - pres - sion, I'm
with His word to guide me, From temp - ta - tions hide me, I'm
close is our re - la - tion, Firm is its foun - da - tion, So
F Dm B♭m6/D♭ F/C C7 F B♭ F
stand - ing on the Sol - id Rock.
stand - ing on the Sol - id Rock.
on this Sol - id Rock I'll stay.

CHORUS

C7 F
I'm stand - - ing on the Rock of A - ges,
Stand-ing on the Rock On the Rock of A - ges,
C7 F
Safe from all the storm that ra - ges,
Safe from ev - 'ry storm, All the storm that ra - ges,
C♯o Dm
Rich but not from Sa - tan's wa - ges, I'm
Rich in love, I'm rich, Not from Sa - tan's wa - ges,
F Dm B♭m6/D♭ F/C C7 F B♭ F
stand - ing on the Sol - id Rock.

I'M GONNA LOVE HIM

Words and Music by LANNY WOLFE

Arr. by W. Elmo Mercer

G7/D
G6(♭9)
G+(♭9)
G
C(sus)
Cm
prove His great___ love,___ the Sav-ior chose___ the hard-est
more___ can I trust Him___ to care for___ His
day___ or a week,___ or a month or___ a
Cm(maj7)
Cm7
F9
F9 (+11)
F9
F7
Fm7/B♭
way; On Cal-v'ry's tree___ all of His life___ He gave for me.___
own? How___ much more___ will He an-swer___ when I call?___
year, Could I ev-er___ re-pay,___ that's why I say:___
CHORUS
B♭7
A♭/B♭
E♭
A♭maj7/E♭
E♭
So I'm gon-na love Him, I'm gon-na love Him,
I'm___ gon-na trust Him, I'm gon-na trust Him,
I'm___ gon-na serve Him, I'm gon-na serve Him,

Abmaj7/Eb Eb Bbm6/Db C7 C7+ C7 Fm Fm6 Fm7 Bb° Bb9
I'm gon-na love Him all of my life; — I'm gon - na
I'm gon-na trust Him all of my life; — I'm gon - na
I'm gon-na serve Him all of my life; — I'm gon - na
Fm Bb° Bb9 Fm Bb° Bb9
love Him, I'm gon-na love Him, I'm gon - na
trust Him, I'm gon-na trust Him, I'm gon - na
serve Him, I'm gon-na serve Him, I'm gon - na
Fm Bb9 Gm/Bb Bb7 1-2 Eb Ab/Eb 3 Eb rit.
love Him all of my life. 2. If He
trust Him all of my life. 3. How could I
serve Him all of my life.
1-2
3
rit.

Slower
C9
F
Bbmaj7
F
I'm gon-na love Him,
I'm gon-na trust Him,
Cm6
Eb
D7 D7+ D7
Gm Gm6 Gm7
C° C9
I'm gon-na serve Him all of my life;
I'm gon-na
Am
C
C7
love Him,
I'm gon-na trust Him,
I'm gon-na serve Him
all of my life!

BLESSIN' AFTER BLESSIN'

Words and Music by JOHN STALLINGS
Arr. by W. Elmo Mercer

E♭
If you're not hap - py, got a Friend I want you to meet;
A♭
C7/G
Fm
A♭
A°7
Since I met Je - sus,
2nd time to ⊕
E♭/B♭
B♭m6/D♭
C+
Gm/C
Fm
Gm/F
A♭/B♭
B♭7
E♭
bless - in' aft - er bless - in' keep on fol - low - in' me!
E♭
E°7
Fm7
Fm7/C
B♭7
(Spoken) You know, I don't deserve it, but that's just the way it's been!

Fm
Fm
E♮
Fm
E♭
B♭7
E♭
Since the night I met the Lord, it all start - ed back then;
E♭
Fm
E♭
G
Be - fore I got saved I did-n't have an ounce of vic - to - ry,
A♭
C7
G
Fm
A♭
A°7
Since I met Je - sus,
E♭
B♭
B♭m6
D♭
C+
Gm
C
Fm
Gm
F
A♭
B♭
B♭7
E♭
E♭
bless - in' aft - er bless-in' keep on fol-low-in' me!
8

I SAW YOU

Words, Music and Arr. by SONJA NELSON SCHWAB

17
Bb Fm7 Bb7 Fm7 Bb7 Eb7 Fm Eb/G
peace and real con - tent - ment set - tled o - ver me. I
how it must have hurt You when they nailed Him to a cross. I
Ab Ab+ Ab6 A0 Eb/Bb Gm Cm
saw You in the sun - set, in the em - ber's fi - nal glow. I
saw the crowd as they jeered Him hang - ing on the cross in shame. I
mf
F9 Cm7 F7 2nd time to Bb7
saw You ev'-ry - where Lord; You were there and now I know I
felt the pain of those nail-prints And I'll nev - er be the
2nd time to
8va
mf
29
Eb Bb6 Eb7 Ab F9
love You Lord, and I thank You for ev - er - y thing You do. But
mp

B♭7 Fm7 B♭7 F♯m Fm7 B♭13 B♭7 E♭ A♭ B♭13 D.S.
most of all I love You, just for be-ing You. I
D.S.
CODA
B♭7 B7 E EM7 E7
same, I'll nev-er be the same. Oh, I love You, Lord, and I thank You for
8va
f
ff
A F♯7 B BM7 B7
ev'-ry thing You do. But most of all I love You
mp
F♯m7 B13 B7 E
just for be-ing You.
8va
15ma

I LIVE

Words and Music by RICH COOK

G G/B C Bm/D D7 G Dsus G D/F♯ G7
live, I live to wor - ship Him. Thank You Je - sus, thank You
C A9/C♯ D Em Am/C E7/B Am G/D Em Am/C E/B Am
Je - sus; Be - cause You're a - live, be - cause You're a -
G/D Em Am/G E/B Am Bm/D C/D A°/D G D♭/E♭ A♭/E♭ E♭7
live, Be - cause You're a - live. I live. I
A♭ A♭/C D♭ E♭ D♭/E♭ E♭7 A♭ A♭7/E♭ D♭/E♭ A♭ A♭/C D♭
live, I live be - cause He is ris - en, I live, I live with

Eb Db/Eb Eb7 Ab Ab/F Eb Ab Db/Ab Ab7/C Db Eb Ab Ab7/Eb Db/Eb
pow'r o - ver sin; I live, I live be - cause He is ris-en, I
Ab Ab/C Db Cm/Eb Eb7 Ab Ebsus rall. Ab Absus Bb9/F Eb/G Ab7/Gb
live, I live to wor - ship Him. Thank You Je - sus, thank You
rall.
Db/F Db9/F Bb9/D Eb Fm Bbm/Db F/C Bbm Ab/Eb Fm Bbm/Db F/C Bbm
Je - sus, be - cause You're a - live, be - cause You're a -
Ab/Eb Fm Bbm/Db F/C Bbm Ebsus Ebsus/Bb Eb Ab Gb/Ab Ab
live, be - cause You're a - live I live!
8va
8va

MY HOUSE IS FULL (But My Field is Empty)

Words and Music by LANNY WOLFE
Arranged by W. Elmo Mercer

Db7 Gb Fm Ebm7 Ab13 Db6/9
laugh-ter as the hours pass by, But a hush calms the
har-vest, but the reap-ers, where are they? In the house, oh, can't the
Bbm7 A7 Db/Ab Fm/Ab Ab7 Db Ab7 Ebm7/Bb Ab7/C
sing-ing as the Fa-ther sad-ly cries:
chil-dren hear the Fa-ther sad-ly say:
CHORUS
rall.
Db Db/Eb F Gb Db a tempo Gb/Ab
"My house is full, but my field is emp-ty;
a tempo
Db Db/C Bb Ab Ab7 Ebm7/Bb Ab7/C
Who will go and work for me to-day? It

D♭ D♭/E♭ F G♭ D♭ B♭m A7
seems my chil - dren all want to stay a-round my ta-ble, — But
D♭/A♭ E♭m7 F7(♯5) B♭m A7
no one — wants to work in my field, —
D♭/A♭ E♭m7 G♭/A♭
No one — wants to work in — my field."
1
D♭ A♭7 E♭m7/B♭ A♭7/C
2
D♭ G♭/A♭ D.S.
field." 2. Push a-
3
D♭ Fine
field." —
8

MORE OF YOU

Words by GLORIA GAITHER

Music by WILLIAM J. GAITHER
and GARY S. PAXTON

B♭ E♭/F B♭ F13 B♭ Dm
new. I'm not seek - ing a gift or e - mo - tion-al lift, But one
pair. Yet my thirst drives me on and I stum - ble a - long O - ver
Fm G7 Cm Cm/B♭ A♭
thing I'm long - ing to do Is to lift up my cup and let
ground so bar - ren and dry; For the spring's just a - head Liv - ing
F7 Cm7 F13 Cm/F B♭ Cm/B♭ B♭maj7 Cm/B♭ B♭ F13 B♭
Chorus
You fill it up with just You!
Wa - ter! "Lord, fill me," I cry.
More of You,
mf
B♭7 E♭ G7/D Cm Cm7 F7
more of You - I've had all, but what I

Cm7 Eb/F F6 F9 Bb F13
need — just more of You. Of things I've
Eb/Bb Bb Bb7 Bb7/D Eb G7/D
had my fill and yet I hun - ger still;
3
Cm Cm7 F7 Cm7 F7
Emp - ty and bare, Lord, hear my prayer for more of
1 Bb Cm/Bb Bbmaj7 Cm/Bb Bb F13 mp D.S.
2 Bb Bb7 C7/Bb Ebm6/Bb Bb Fine
You. 2. I have You.
D.S. mp poco rit. p Fine

IT FEELS SO GOOD

(Just Being Here Again)

Words and Music by LANNY WOLFE
Arr. by W. Elmo Mercer

Eb
Bb+
Eb9
There's just noth - in' I like bet - ter than God's
Ab
Db9
Eb
C7
chil - dren get - tin' to - geth - er, It feels so good just
last time to
Fm
Ab/Bb
Bb7
Eb
VERSE
be - in' here a - gain.
1. Oh, what
(Solo) 2. Just look a -
last time to
Eb
Fm
Fm7
Bb
peace, Oh, what joy, Oh, what
round and you will see Hap - py

Fm
Bb9
Eb
Db/Bb
Fm/Eb
Eb7
ir - re - place - a - ble com - fort I en - joy! When God's
fac - es where sad fac - es used to be; For Je - sus
Ab
Gm
chil - dren get to - geth - er, and sing prais - es to the King,
saved us by His mer - cy, placed us in His fam - i - ly,
Cm
Fm
Ab/Bb
Bb7
This feel - ing I just would - n't trade for an - y - thing!
And now this fel - low - ship means all the world to me.
Eb
It feels so
CODA
Eb
Ab
Eb
CODA

NEVER A MAN SPAKE LIKE THIS MAN

Words and Music by JOEL HEMPHILL, JR.

Eb Eb7 Ab Eb
1. Je - sus went in - to the tem - ple when_ He was on - ly twelve,
2. He calmed the trou - bled wa - ters with a few words from His lips,
Bb
His words awed the el - ders, as His wis - dom they be - held;_____
The lame walked, the dumb_ talked when He said to them,"Be healed!"____
Eb7/Bb Ab Eb Ab
Said the mul - ti - tude that fol - lowed_ to hear the man from Gal - i - lee,
And_ Laz - 'rus came forth from the grave_when He heard the Mas - ter speak,
Abm6 Eb Bb7 Eb
"Nev - er a man spake like this Man; He who said, Come fol - low Me."_____
"Nev - er a man spake like this Man; when He said, Come fol - low Me."_____

CHORUS

Eb7 Ab Eb
Nev-er a man spake like this Man,___ the glo - r'ous King of kings,
Eb7 Ab Eb Bb
He spoke to my trou-bled soul, and now my heart sings;___
Eb Eb7 Ab Eb Ab
He has prom - ised in His ho - ly Word some day His face I'll see,
Abm6 Eb Bb7 Eb Ab Eb
Nev-er a man spake like this Man when He said, "Come,fol - low Me."___

RIGHT IN THE MIDDLE OF MY NEED

Words and Music by JOHN STALLINGS
Arr. by W. Elmo Mercer

trou-ble that I thought God was far a-way.
God He finds me right in the mid-dle of my need.
CHORUS
Right in the mid-dle of my prob-lem was a Man with the
nail-prints in His hands; Just when the pres-sure was the great-est, I heard Him
whis-per, "I un-der-stand." Now you may think that He's far a-way,
shroud-ed in a mys-ter-y, But when I need-ed Je-sus He was
stand-ing right there right in the mid-dle of my need! need!
D. S.

BUILD MY MANSION
(Next Door to Jesus)

Words and Music by DOTTIE RAMBO

INTRO.
G7 C
C F C
1. I have no cas - tles No earth - ly king - dom
2. My moth - er's man - sion may be close by me
G G7 C
But my cab - in will do 'til I get home.
A - cross the gold - - - en av - e - nue.
G7 C7 F C
My man - sion's yon - der on the hills of Glo - ry,
She was the first one to teach me of Heav - en
3
3

G7 C
Oh, I hope my man - sion sits near God's Throne.
And the ver - y first one, Lord, to tell me 'bout you.
CHORUS
G7 C7 F C
Build my man - sion next door to Je - sus
G7 C
And tell the an - gels I'm com - ing home.
G7 C7 F C
It does - n't mat - ter who lives a - round me.
G7 C F C
Just so my man - sion sits near the Throne.

HERE WE ARE

Words and Music by DALLAS HOLM
Arr. by Jon Sherberg

E
Dadd9
prais - ing Je -
A
A9/4
A
D
- sus,
for the things
3rd time to Coda
E
D/E
E
A
A
A4/2
A
He's brought us through.
D
E
1. I don't have the words to
2. I nev - er thought that it could

A
F#m7
tell You ___ how I feel. ___
be ___ this way. ___
Bm7
E
D
E
E
I just don't ___ know ___ what I ___ can
And I nev - er thought ___ I'd be ___ the
A
A 9 4
A
C#
say. ___ I'm not ___ wor -
one. ___ But You ___ found ___
C# 4 2
C#
F#m
- thy ___ to speak ___ Your Ho - ly Name, ___
___ me ___ dy - ing in ___ my sin. ___

F♯4/2 F♯m B7
Yet You tell
And You looked
A/B B7 E D/F♯ E7/G♯
2nd time D.C. al Coda
me You love me just the same.
at me with love and took me in.
CODA
Dadd9 E D/E E
For the things He's brought us through.
A A4/2 A A9/4 A
rit.

AMAZING GRACE

Early American Melody

Words by JOHN NEWTON

Arranged by W. ELMO MERCER

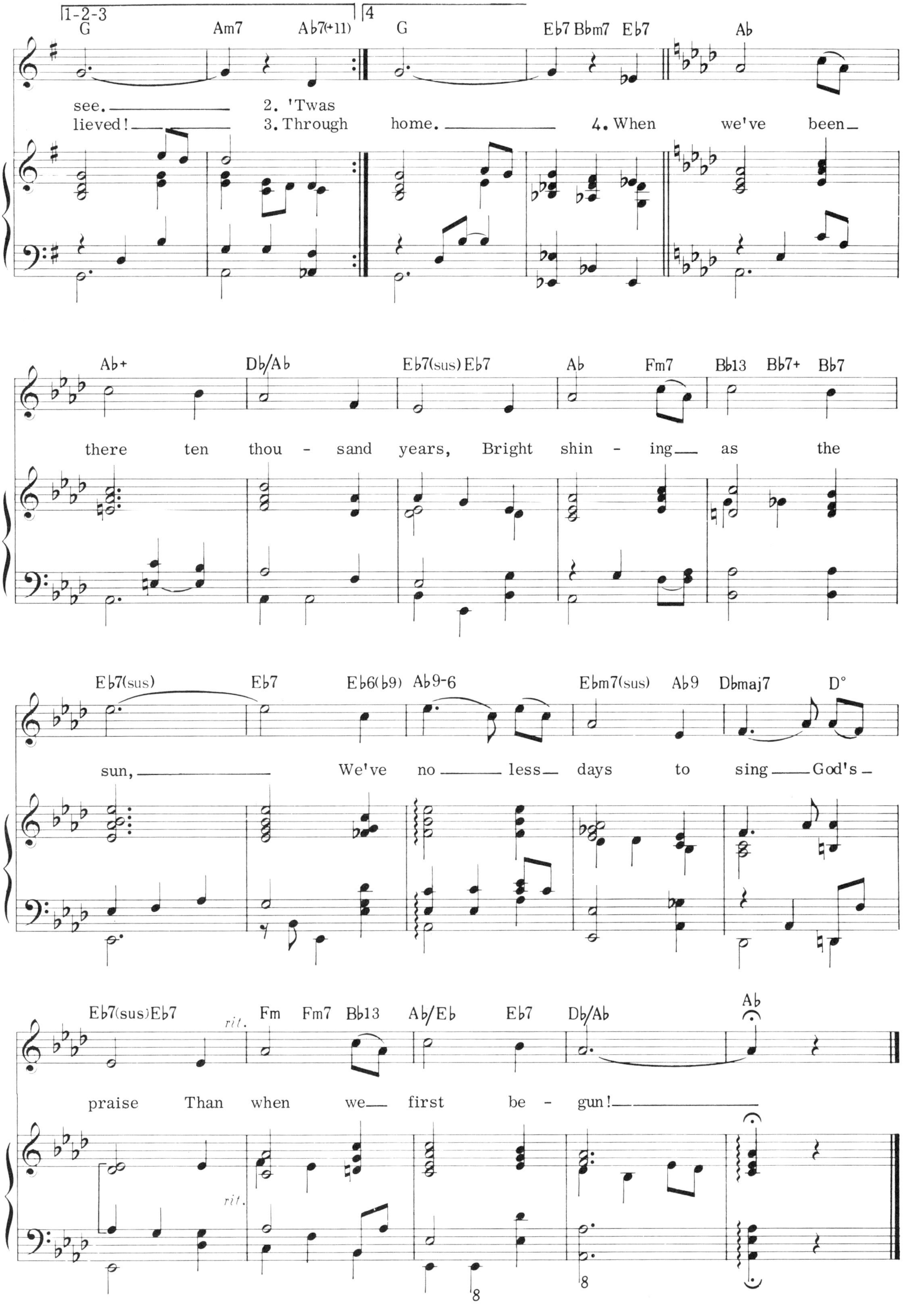
1-2-3
4
G Am7 Ab7(+11) G Eb7 Bbm7 Eb7 Ab
see. 2. 'Twas
lieved! 3. Through home. 4. When we've been
Ab+ Db/Ab Eb7(sus) Eb7 Ab Fm7 Bb13 Bb7+ Bb7
there ten thou - sand years, Bright shin - ing as the
Eb7(sus) Eb7 Eb6(b9) Ab9-6 Ebm7(sus) Ab9 Dbmaj7 D°
sun, We've no less days to sing God's
Eb7(sus) Eb7 rit. Fm Fm7 Bb13 Ab/Eb Eb7 Db/Ab Ab
praise Than when we first be - gun!
rit.
8
8

A BRAND NEW TOUCH

Words and Music by LANNY WOLFE
Arr. by W. Elmo Mercer

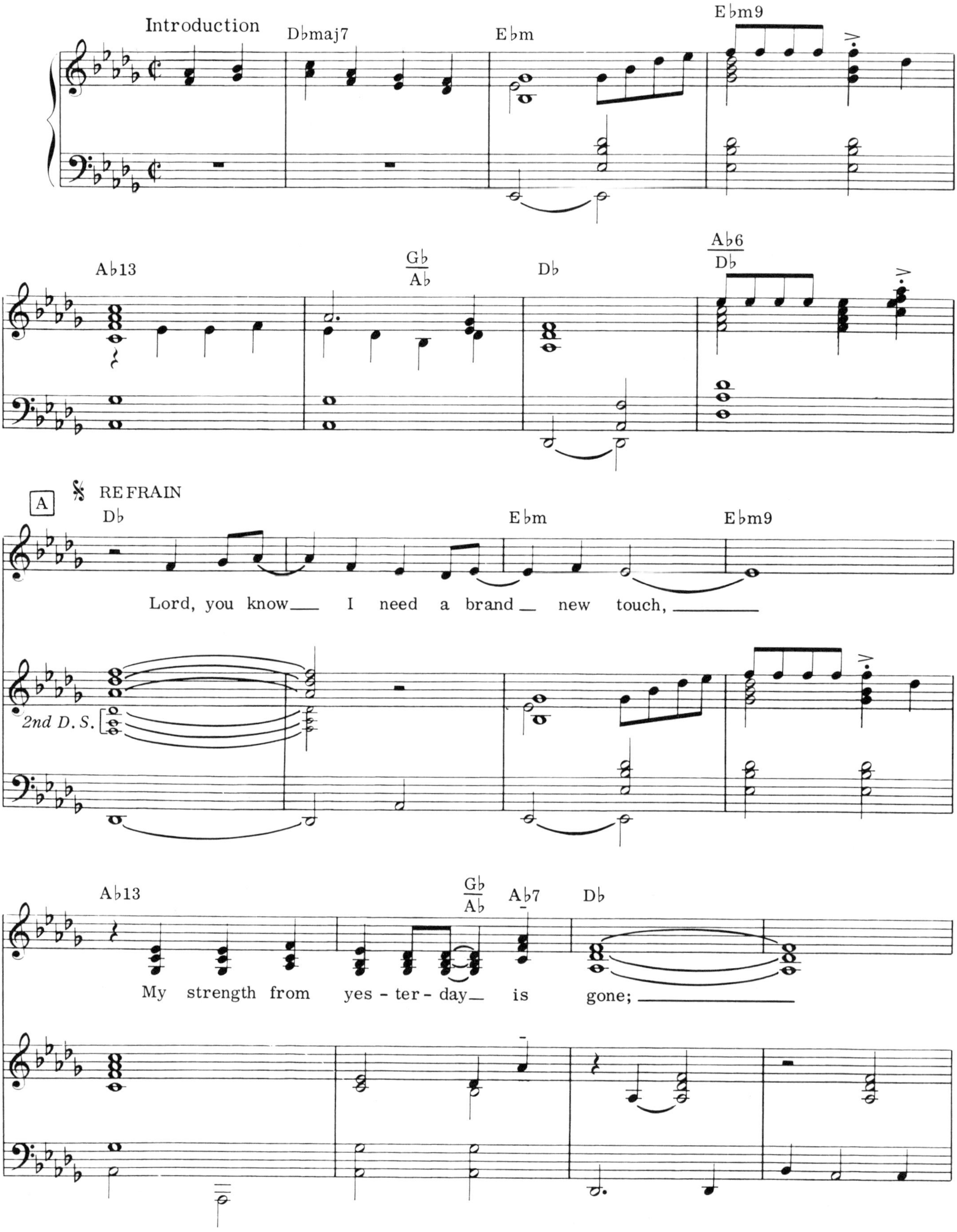

(D♭)
D♭9
E♭m
Em9
But if you'll give me, Lord, an-oth - er touch,
A♭13
G♭/A♭
Last time to ⊕
D♭
3rd time to D
I'll have the strength to car - ry on.
B
D♭maj9
E♭m
Em9
(1) I tho't the sun had come to stay,
(2) Yes - ter-day has come and gone,
A♭13
E♭m7/A♭
A♭7
D♭
But all too soon it went a - way,
And now a new day's com - ing on;

Db maj9
Eb m
Eb m9
And in its place the storm clouds came,
I do not know what it may bring,
Ab7
Gb/Ab
Ab7
Db
Eb m/Db
Db7
And with the clouds there came the rain;
My heart may cry in - stead of sing;
C
Gb
Db
Do7
Eb m
It rained so hard and oh so long,
But midst the storm
But it mat-ters not what comes my way, Lord,
If you'll just touch
Ab7
Db
Db7
Gb
I felt a calm;
It was your touch
me new each day;
Your lov - ing touch

Fm
D°7
E♭m
that bro't me through it all,
With-out your
drives all my fears a-way,
Close by your
A♭7
A♭7/D♭
D♭
D.S. twice
D
G♭
help I'd sure-ly fall.
Lord, you know
side I want to stay.
Fm
D°7
E♭m
A♭7
how weak I real-ly am
E-ven bet-ter than my-
D♭
D♭7
G♭
self!
But with your help I know I

Fm D°7 E♭m E♭m7
real - ly can Make it thro' the dark - est night, Ev-'ry thing's gon-na
D.S. CODA
A♭ Fm G♭ A♭ A♭7 D♭
be al - right; on; If you'll touch me,
E♭m A♭7 G♭/A♭ D♭
Lord, I'll have the strength to car - ry on, Won't you touch me,
E♭m A♭7 rit. G♭/A♭ D♭ Fine
Lord, Give me the strength to car - ry on.
rit.

FOLLOW THE LEADER

Words and Music by DOTTIE RAMBO
Arr. by David Huntsinger

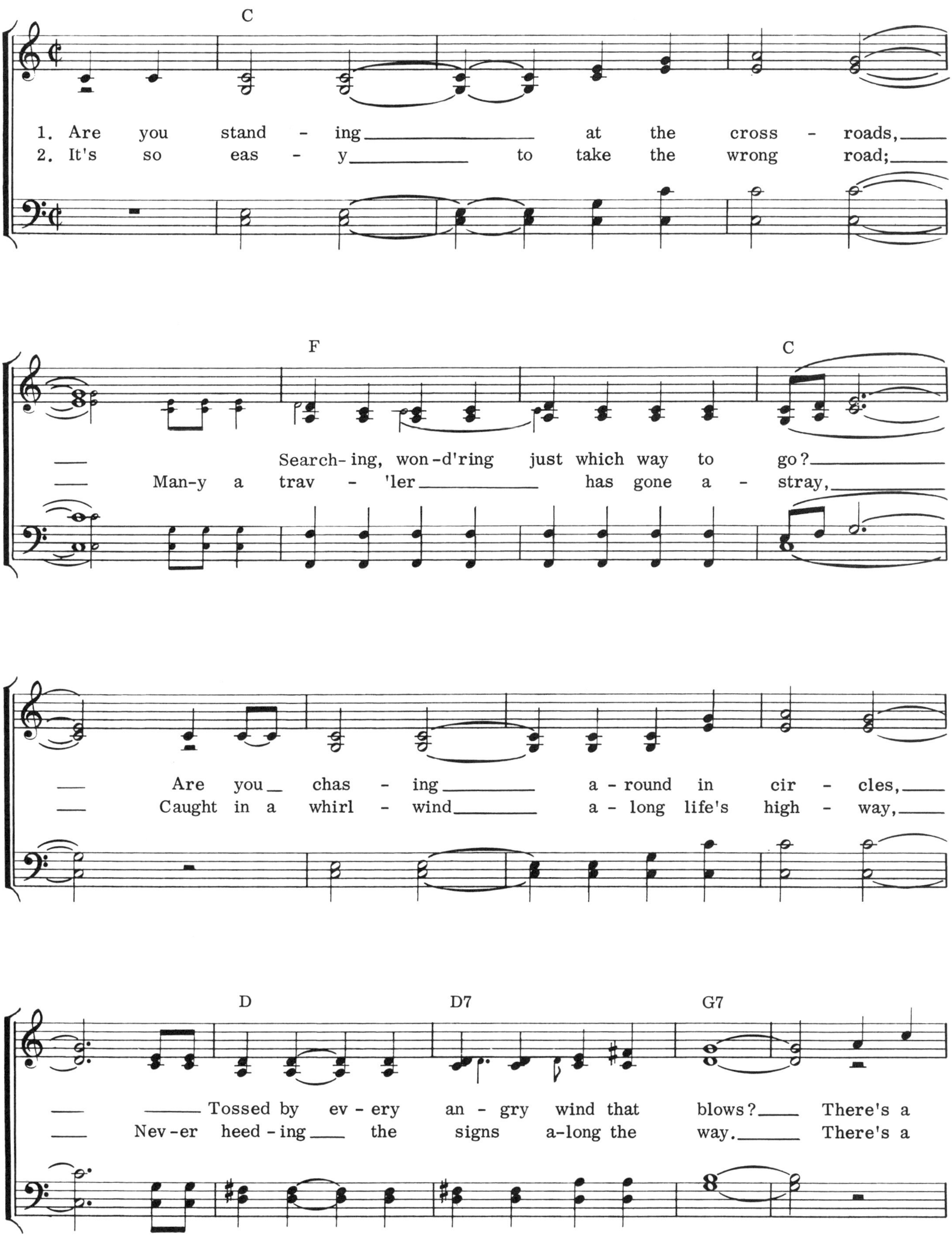
C
1. Are you stand - ing at the cross - roads,
2. It's so eas - y to take the wrong road;
F
C
Search- ing, won-d'ring just which way to go?
Man-y a trav - 'ler has gone a - stray,
Are you chas - ing a - round in cir - cles,
Caught in a whirl - wind a - long life's high - way,
D
D7
G7
Tossed by ev - ery an - gry wind that blows? There's a
Nev-er heed - ing the signs a-long the way. There's a

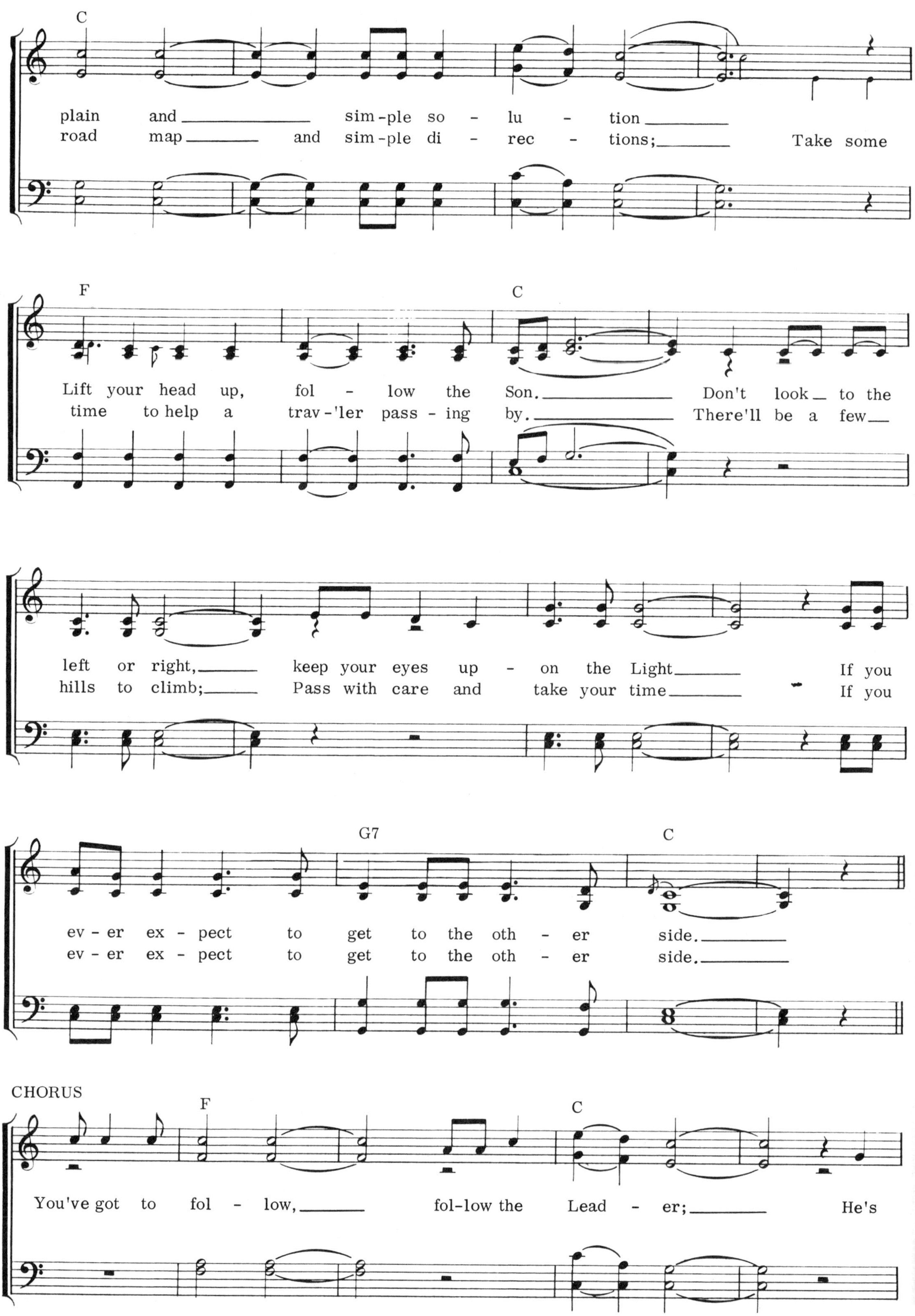
C
plain and sim-ple so - lu - tion
road map and sim-ple di - rec - tions; Take some
F
C
Lift your head up, fol - low the Son. Don't look to the
time to help a trav-'ler pass - ing by. There'll be a few
left or right, keep your eyes up - on the Light If you
hills to climb; Pass with care and take your time If you
G7
C
ev - er ex - pect to get to the oth - er side.
ev - er ex - pect to get to the oth - er side.
CHORUS
F
C
You've got to fol - low, fol-low the Lead - er; He's

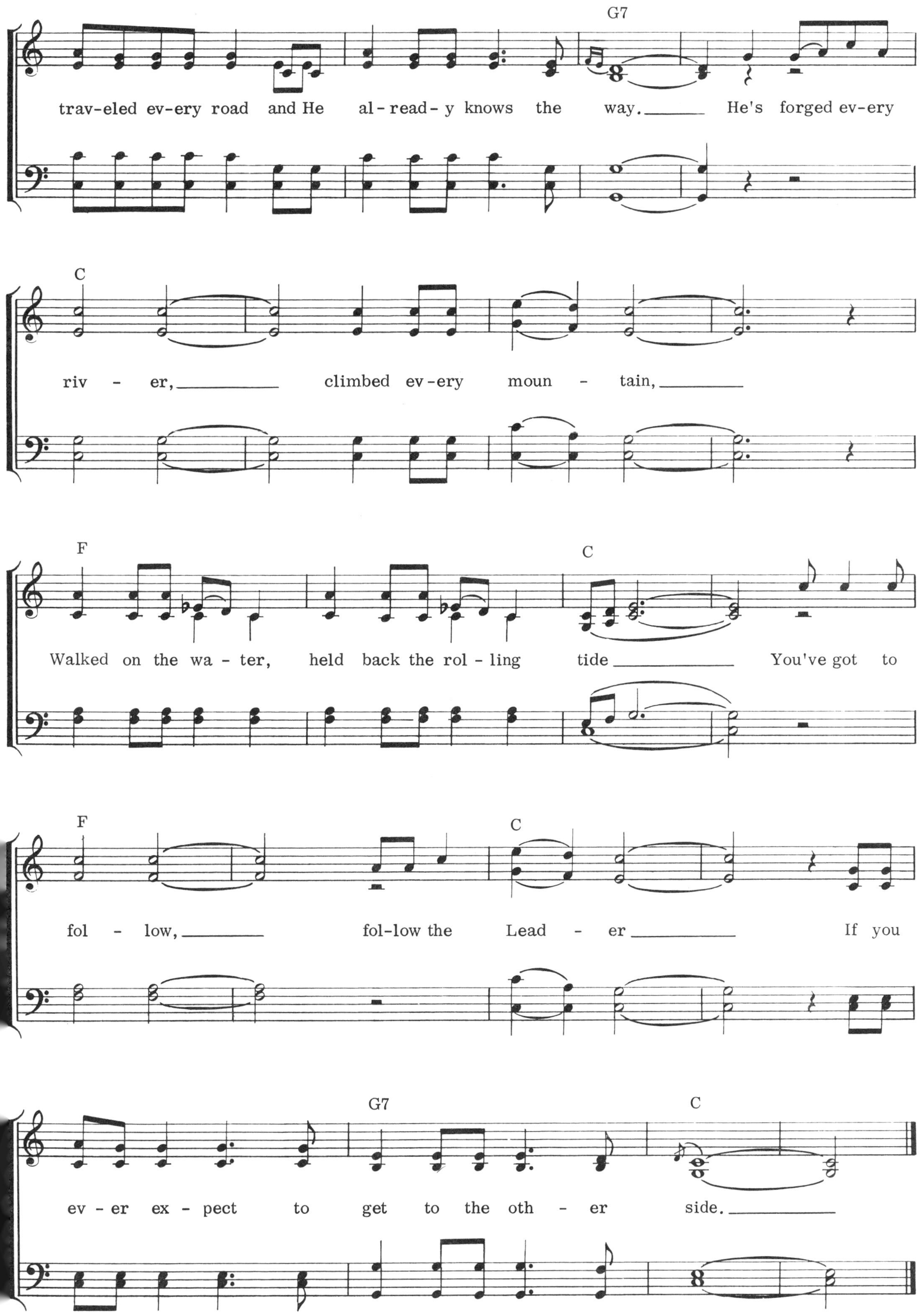
G7
trav-eled ev-ery road and He al-read-y knows the way. He's forged ev-ery
C
riv - er, climbed ev-ery moun - tain,
F
C
Walked on the wa - ter, held back the rol - ling tide You've got to
F
C
fol - low, fol-low the Lead - er If you
G7
C
ev - er ex - pect to get to the oth - er side.

REBORN

Words and Music by STEPHEN R. ADAMS
Arr. by W. Elmo Mercer

Cmaj7 Fm Cmaj7 C Fm6
1. Life was an emp - ty thing filled with re - morse,
2. Gone is the tyr - an - ny of death and de - spair!
C F/C C Fm C A7
Liv - ing had lost its glow, I knew no guid - ing force;
Van - ished, the emp - ti - ness! There's beau - ty ev - 'ry - where!
3

Dm7 B♭9 C E7/B Am
Then I met Je - sus and at His touch di - vine,
Life has new mean-ing, my soul has seen its worth;
Am Am7 D9 F♯o G D13 G7 Dm7 G7
Sud-den-ly I came a - live! New life is mine!
Mir - a - cle of mir - a - cles! I've found new birth!
CHORUS
C C+ F Dm Dm7
Re - born! Re - born in Je - sus,
G7 G7+ C Dm7 G6 G7
Life ev-er - last-ing is mine! And this

C C+ F6 A
life, this life that I live, I live thro' the One Who gives the
Dm A7 F6 C/G F Fm 1 C/G Dm9 G7 C F/C
vic - t'ry, For in Christ I have been re - born!
C D.S. 2 C/G G♯o Am Am7 D9 D7 Fm6
been re - born; For in
C/G F G6 G7 C Fine
Christ I have been re - born!
8va

LIFT HIM UP

Words and Music by REBA RAMBO GARDNER
Arranged by David Huntsinger

OPEN MY EYES

Words and Music by CANDY HEMPHILL

F C7
1. Lord, I saw how you used ole Mo - ses,
2. Lord, have Your way; I'm just a ves-sel that You made,
B♭ C7 F
How he led Your chil - dren out of mis - er - y;
I don't have a lot to of - fer, I'm just clay;
Fmaj7 B♭maj7 B♭ F F7
But I'm un - worth - y to do such a deed, But while I'm
But let me see just what You would have me be, Give me the
B♭ C7 F
here, I'm sure there's a job for me.
word, and I'll say what You'd have me say.

CHORUS

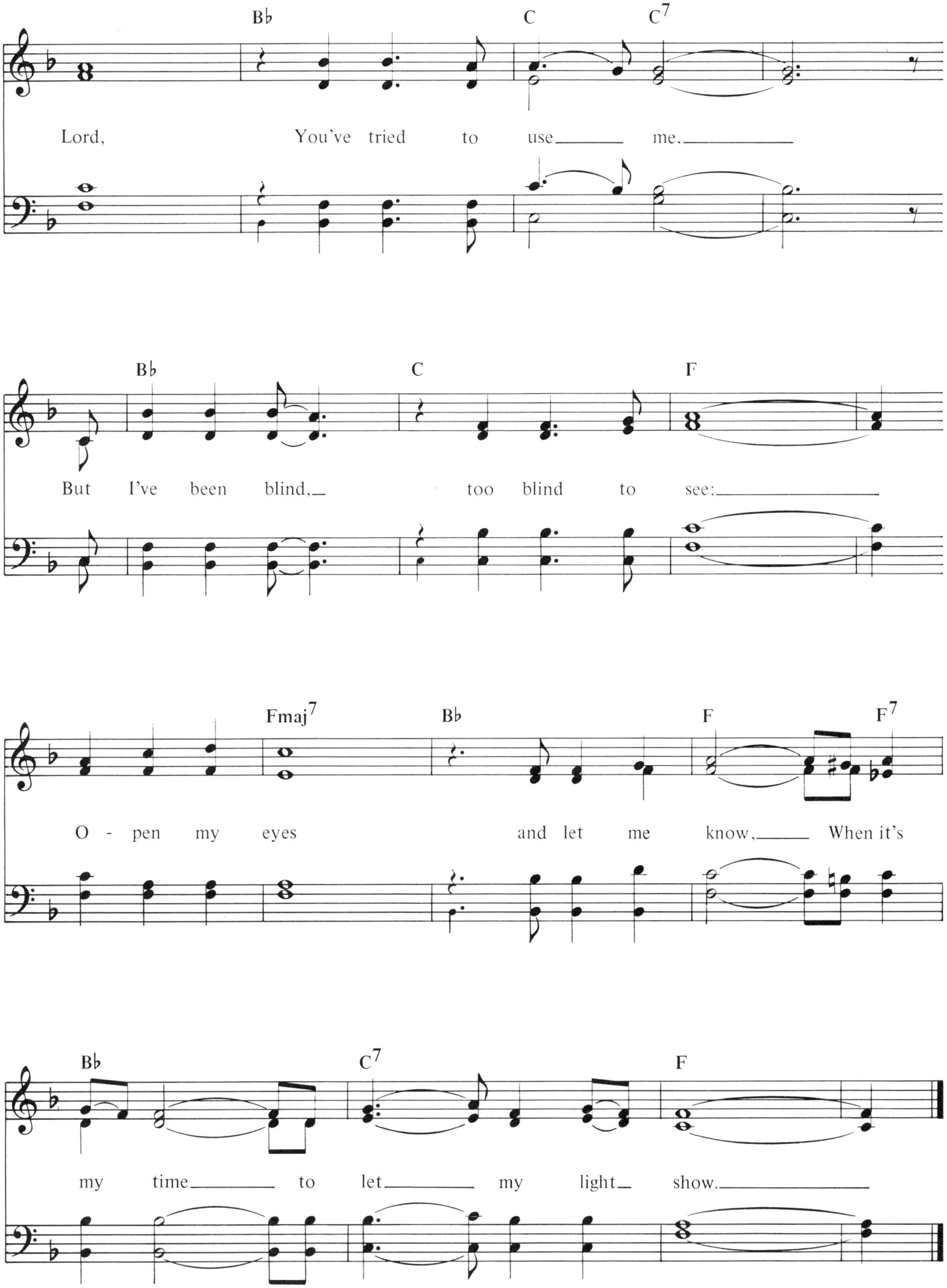
B♭ C C7
Lord, You've tried to use me,
B♭ C F
But I've been blind, too blind to see:
Fmaj7 B♭ F F7
O - pen my eyes and let me know, When it's
B♭ C7 F
my time to let my light show.

BORN TO DIE

Anonymous
Arr. by Lanny Wolfe

Lightly
G G°/B♭ D7/A Am7 D7 Cm6/D D7(♭9) G(add 9) G
G(add 9) G G G♯° Am D7 C/G G G/B
1. Ev - 'ry mo - ment there are new lives born in this world, For the
2. Long be - fore earth was fash - ioned, God knew our need, And He
C Am7 D9 C/G G G♯° Am7 D7
pur - pose of liv - ing and all of life's joys to know; But the
willed that His Son would be slain for the sins of man; So that
G G♯° Am D9 G G/B C C♯° G/D G Dm6/F
dear Son of God came down from on high With one rea - son for
we might have life on - ly He could sup - ply; Oh, what love, and what

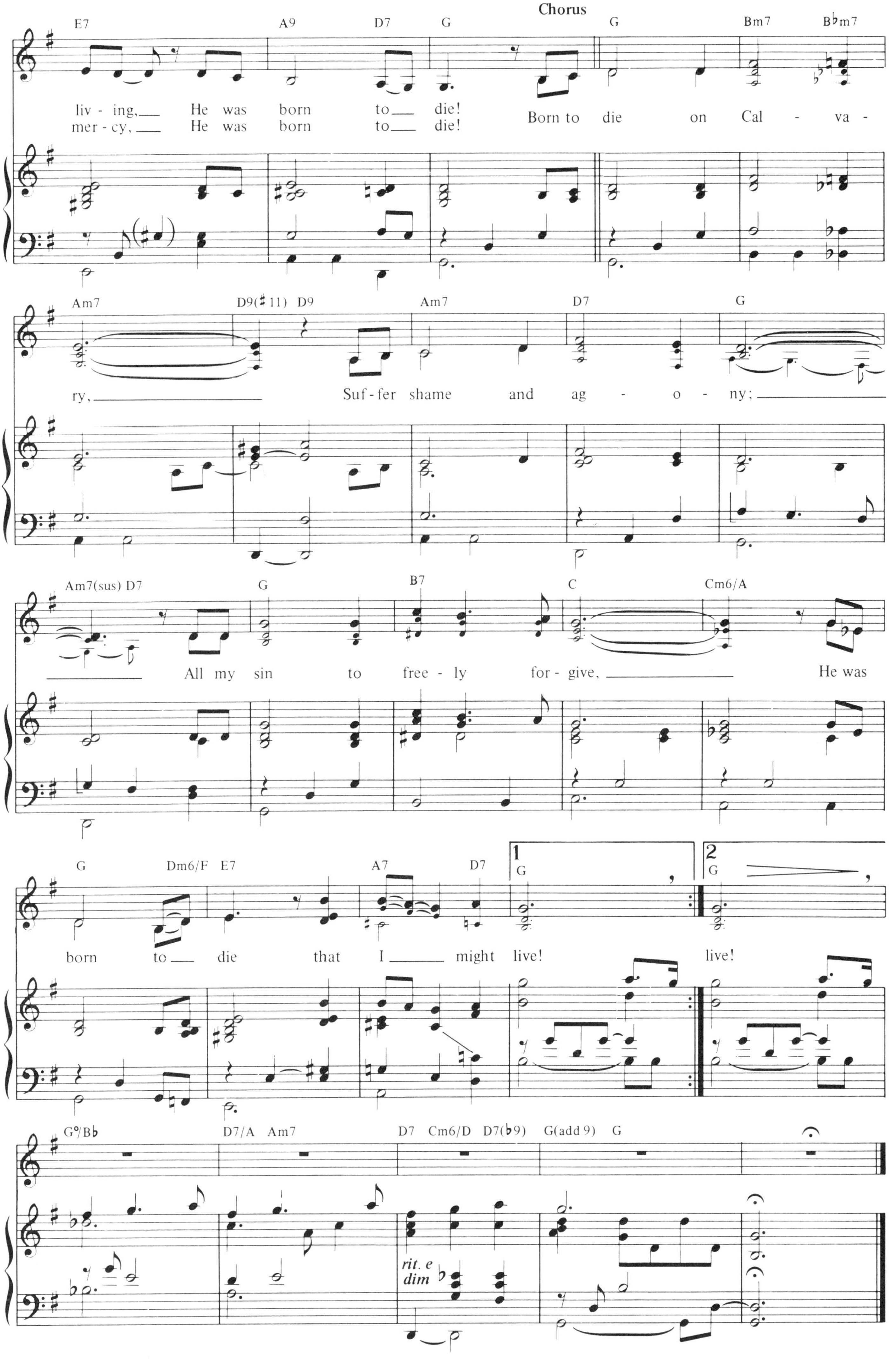

Chorus
E7 A9 D7 G
G Bm7 B♭m7
liv - ing, He was born to die!
mer - cy, He was born to die!
Born to die on Cal - va -
Am7 D9(♯11) D9 Am7 D7 G
ry, Suf - fer shame and ag - o - ny;
Am7(sus) D7 G B7 C Cm6/A
All my sin to free - ly for - give, He was
G Dm6/F E7 A7 D7
1 G
2 G
born to die that I might live!
live!
G°/B♭ D7/A Am7 D7 Cm6/D D7(♭9) G(add 9) G
rit. e dim

CLOSER TO YOU

Words and Music by DAVE CLARK

F
C
C7
1. I know that I've failed you, Lord, time and a - gain.
2. Lord, I sur - ren - der all that I am,
F
But each time You al - ways stayed true:
For what - ev - er You'd have me do;
C
C7
And that's why I kneel at the cross once a - gain,
I've faith in Your prom - ise, I know that You'll show
F
And ask to draw clos - er to You.
A way to draw clos - er to You.

CHORUS

F Bb F C C7
Clos - er to You, Lord, Clos - er I pray,
Bb F Fdim F
Help me draw clos - er to Your will to - day;
F7 Bb D7 Gm
It does - n't mat - ter what oth - ers may do,
C7 F
I want to draw clos - er to You.

HE WAS THE TALK OF THE TOWN

Words and Music by DOTTIE RAMBO
Arr. by David Huntsinger

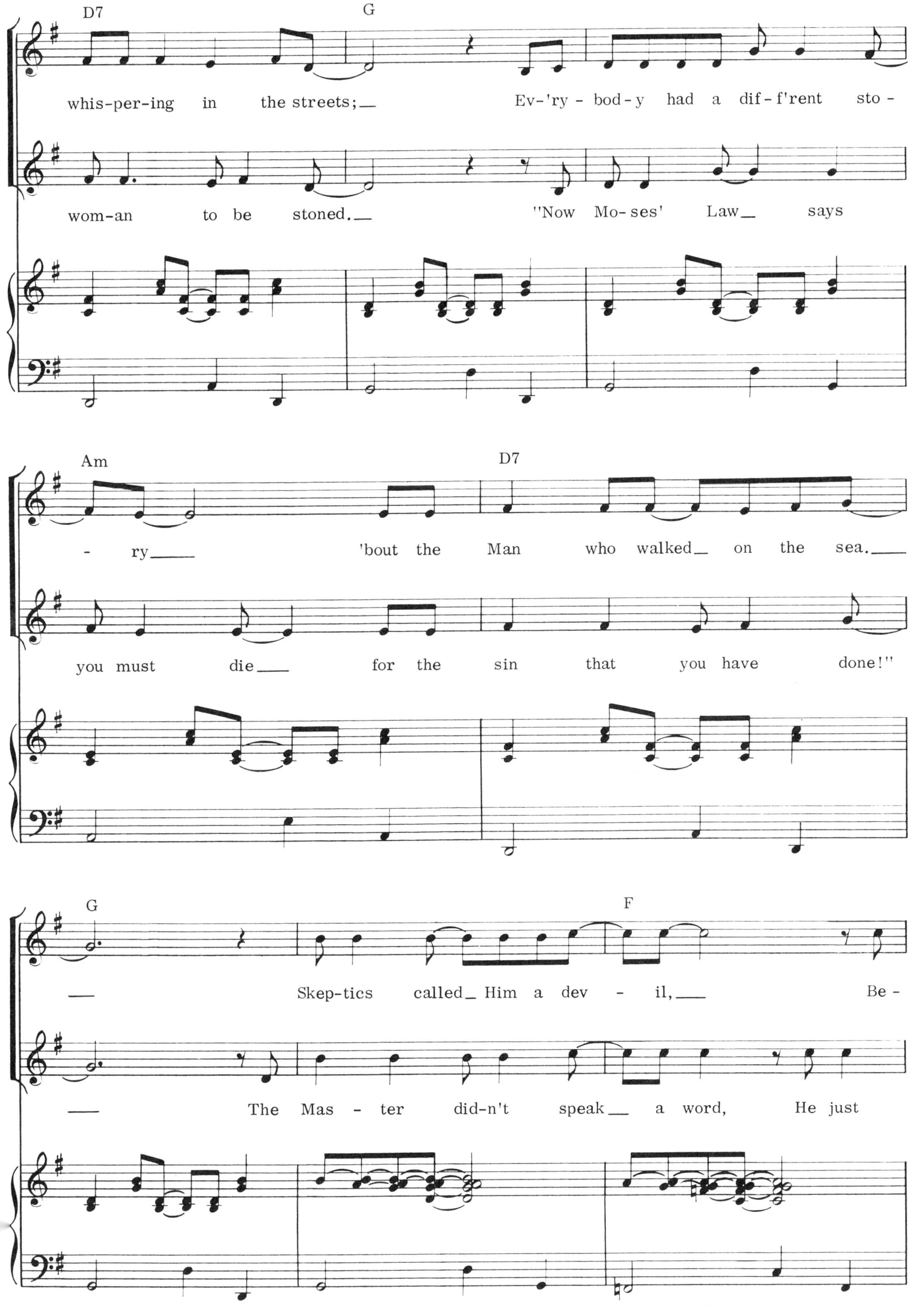
D7
G
whis-per-ing in the streets; Ev-'ry-bod-y had a dif-f'rent sto-
wom-an to be stoned. "Now Mo-ses' Law says
Am
D7
-ry 'bout the Man who walked on the sea.
you must die for the sin that you have done!"
G
F
Skep-tics called Him a dev-il, Be-
The Mas-ter did-n't speak a word, He just

C G C
liev - ers fol-lowed Him 'round._ He was a Man of fame,_ the dev - il
wrote up - on the ground._ When they read the news_ there was
G D7 G
to Chorus
knew Him by name;_ He was the talk_ of the town.
to Chorus
none to ac-cuse;_ He was the talk_ of the town.
CHORUS
G Am D7
He was the talk_ of the town. Some folks lift - in' Him up,_
Oth- er folks_ put - tin' Him down,_

G C D7
Heal-ing the lame_ at the tem - ple,_ De - liv-'ring the souls_that were bound;_
G C G
_ He was a Man of fame,_The dev-il knew Him by name;_
D7 1. G to 2nd Verse
He was the talk_ of the town. 2. The
2. G D7 G
town. He was the talk_ of the town._

COUNTRY CHURCH

Words, Music and Arr. by JERRY NELSON

*G/A♭ G7/A♭7 C/D♭ C♯o/Do G/D/A♭/E A7/B♭7 D7/E♭7 G/A♭ D7/E♭7
1. I was
2. (From the)
G/A♭ G7/A♭7 C/D♭
driv - in' down the val - ley with my ra - di - o on, try - in' hard to change my dismal state of
mo-ment that I stepped in-side that lit - tle coun-try church, I felt a warmth I nev-er felt be-
G/A♭ G/A♭ E7/F7
mind. But the mu - sic couldn't cov - er all my shat-tered dreams or the
fore; And the glow of shin-ing fac - es I could-n't un-der-stand, but it
A7/B♭7 D7/E♭7 G/A♭
emp- ty, emp-ty feel-ing deep in - side. I was tempt-ed to a - ban-don an - y
start-ed something knockin' at my door. Well, the par-son was-n't talk-in 'bout re-

*It is suggested that the first verse and chorus be sung in G, using the optional chords for that key.

G7 / A♭7
C / D♭
B7 / C7
hope I had when I reached to turn my ra - di - o down just e -
lig - ion that day, 'cause the ser - mon hit my con-science like a knife. It was a
E7 / F7
A7 / B♭7
D7 / E♭7
nough to hear the mu - sic from a coun-try church that was sit - tin' on the edge of
heart to heart ex-per - i - ence with God Him - self that would change the whole complexion of my
G / A♭
C / D♭
2nd time to
"Leaning on the Everlasting Arms"
(Hoffmann/Showalter)
town. They were sing - ing
life. They were sing - ing
What a fel - low - ship! What a joy di - vine!
Lean - ing on the ev - er - last - ing arms.
What a bless-ed-ness!
What a peace is mine! Lean - ing on the ev-er - last - ing arms.

"There Is Power in the Blood" (Jones)
E♭7
D.S.
A♭
A♭7
D♭
A♭
2. From the Pow'r, pow'r, Won-der-work-ing pow'r in the
D.S.
E♭7
A♭
A♭7
Blood of the Lamb. There is pow'r, pow'r,
D♭
A♭
B♭m
E♭7
A♭
Won-der-work-ing pow'r in the prec - ious Blood of the Lamb.
E7
A
A7
3. Now I'm driv - in' up the val - ley feel - in' light - er than air I can
D7
A
hard-ly keep 'er un - der fif - ty - five 'Cause I got a taste of hea - ven in a

F♯7
B7
E7
coun-try church where the folks are real-ly com-in' a-live. Something
A
A7
D
hap-pened in that meet-in' on the edge of town and it real-ly, real-ly blew my mind,
C♯7
F♯7
B7
'Cause it changed the whole com-plex-ion of my bro-ken dreams;
E7
A
F7
it's the clos-est thing to hea-ven I can find. I'm sing-in'
B♭
E♭
B♭
What a fel-low-ship! What a joy di-vine! Lean-ing on the ev-er-

F7 B♭ B♭7 E♭
last - ing arms. What a bless- ed - ness! What a peace is mine!
B♭ F7 B♭ B♭ B♭7 E♭
Lean - ing on the ev - er - last - ing arms. Lean - ing, lean - ing;
B♭ F7 B♭ F7 B♭ B♭7 E♭
Safe and se - cure from all a - larms. Lean - ing, lean - ing;
B♭ B♭/F F7 B♭
Lean - ing on the ev - er - last - ing arms.
G♭ A♭ B♭
Ev - er - last - ing arms.

HAVE A NICE DAY WITH JESUS

Words and Music by LANNY WOLFE
Arr. by W. Elmo Mercer

3rd time to 𝄌
C7/E F7 B♭7 A♭/B♭ E♭ A♭7/E♭ E♭
1st time
E♭
with Je - sus, have a nice day!
(1) You can wake up
2nd time
(2) An-y-one can sing when the
3rd time to 𝄌
A♭7
ev - 'ry morn - in' with a smile up - on your face,
sun is shin - in' and ev-'ry-thing seems to be al - right;
E♭
Cm7
Just to know the Lord has kept you one more
But it's a dif-f'rent sto-ry when you're talk-in' 'bout a rain - y

B♭7(sus) B♭7 E♭ E♭7/G
day; And no mat - ter what the day may bring
day; Just let the Lord be your um - brel - la,
A♭ E♭/B♭ Cm
you can face it with a smile, For the Lord will walk be-side
And He'll take you through the storm, Give the world a smile and let
E♭/B♭ B♭7 A♭/B♭ A♭ E♭/G Fm7 E♭
you all the way. Have a nice
them hear you say: Have a nice
E♭
8va

DON'T LIFT THE ANCHOR

Words and Music by DOTTIE RAMBO

C F C
1. Who is that yon-der In the like-ness of Je - sus,
2. The sick and the wea - ry, The tired and the home - sick,
F C D7 G
Stand-ing in the ves - sel that's pull - ing a - shore?
Wait - ing to sail on the old Ship of Zion,
C
Thou - sands are gath - 'ring, It's like a
Leav - ing be - hind them All
F C F
fam - 'ly re un - ion. They're sing - ing a
earth - ly pos - ses - sions In ex - change for a
C F C
new song, Some-thing 'bout go - ing home;
trea - sure Be - yond all earth's mea - sure As they

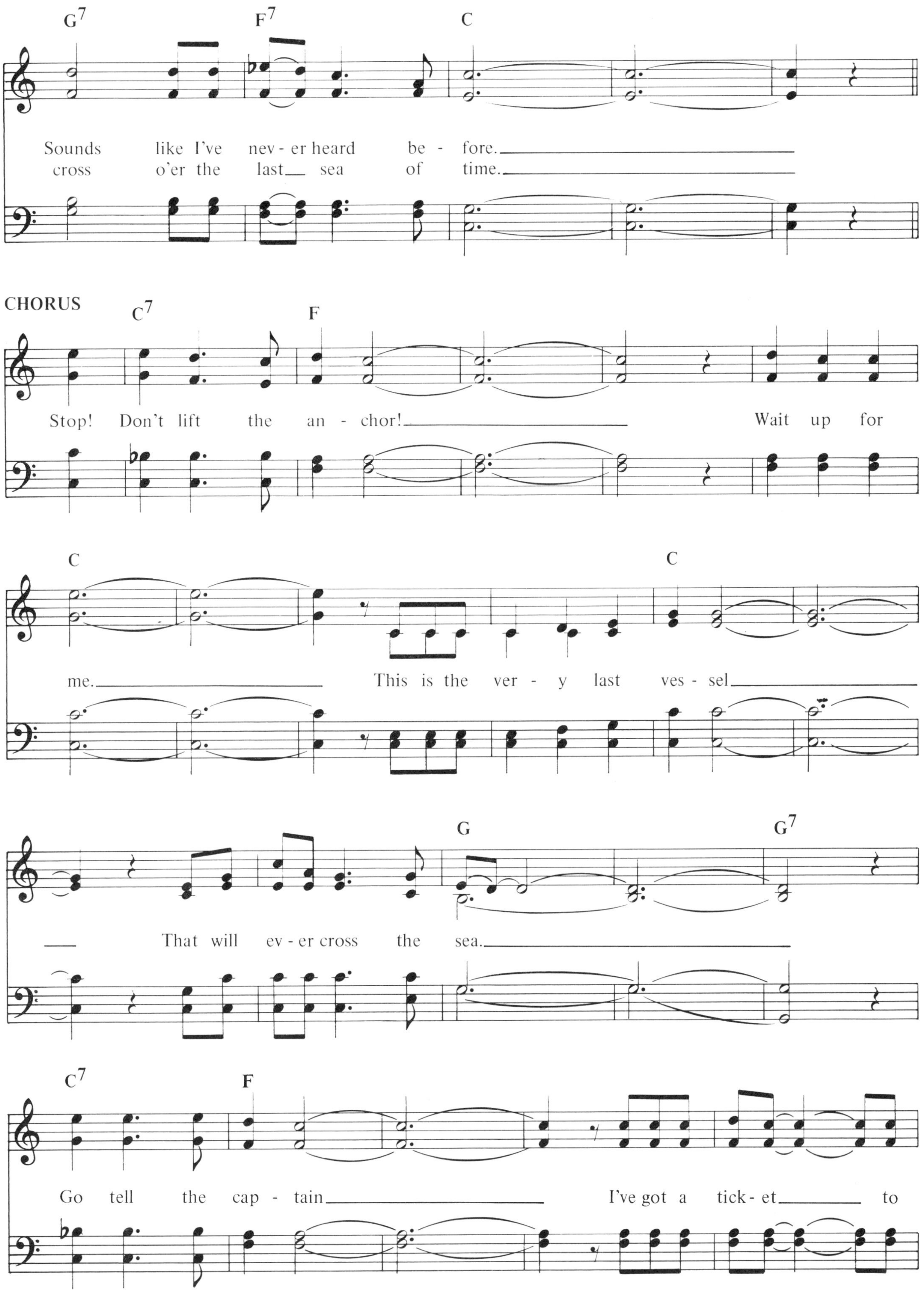
G7 F7 C
Sounds like I've nev-er heard be-fore.
cross o'er the last sea of time.
CHORUS
C7 F
Stop! Don't lift the an-chor! Wait up for
C C
me. This is the ver-y last ves-sel
G G7
That will ev-er cross the sea.
C7 F
Go tell the cap-tain I've got a tick-et to

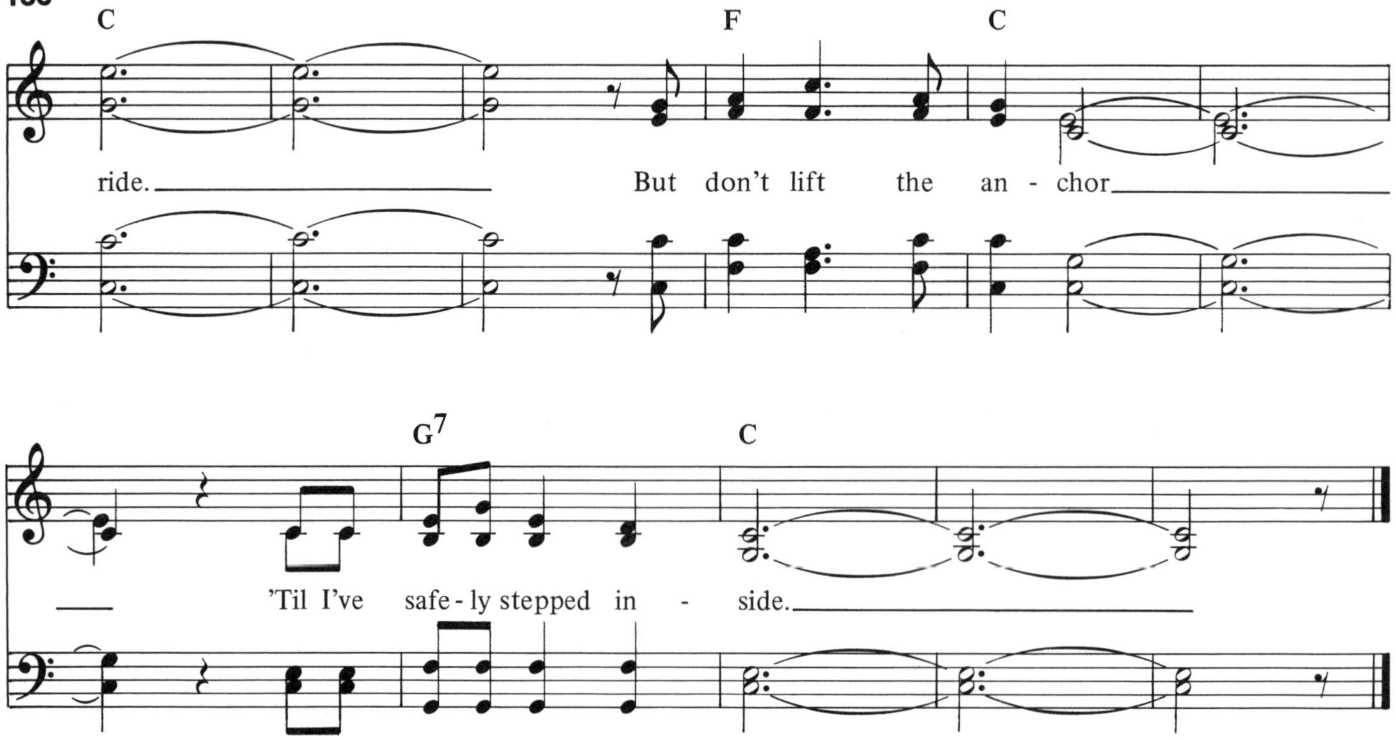
C F C
ride. But don't lift the an - chor
G7 C
'Til I've safe - ly stepped in - side.

TEN THOUSAND YEARS

Words and Music by ELMER COLE
Arr. by W. Elmo Mercer

F C7 F7 B♭
1. Soon I'll come to the end of my jour - ney,
2. We will just be - gin to sing love's sweet sto - ry,
B♭m6 F A7/E Dm G7 C7sus
And I'll meet the One who gave His life for me;
It's a song that the an - gels can - not sing;
C7 B♭/C C7 F C7 F7 B♭
I will thank Him for the love that He gave me,
"I'm re - deemed by the blood of the Sav - ior",

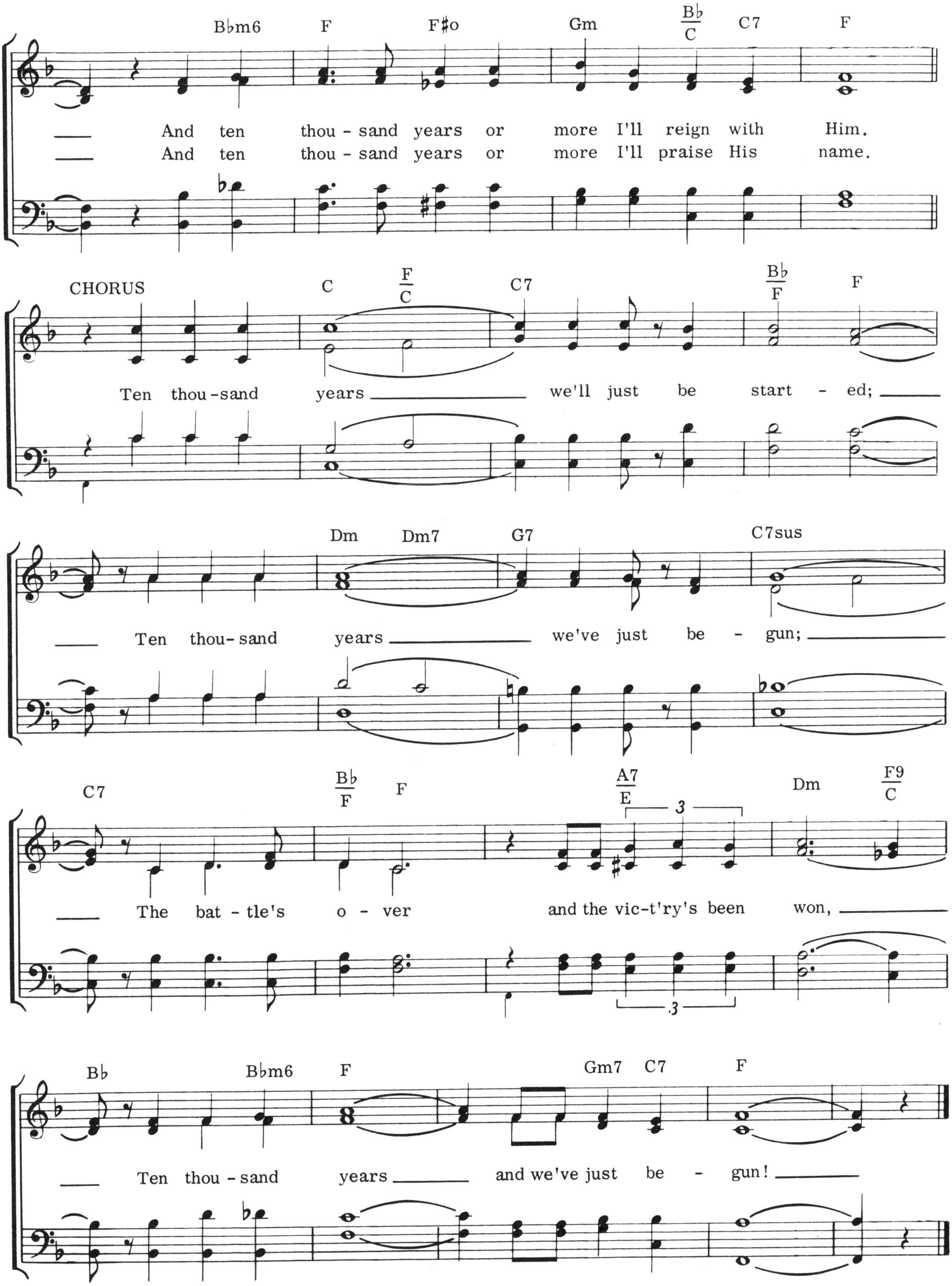
Bbm6 F F#o Gm Bb/C C7 F
And ten thou - sand years or more I'll reign with Him.
And ten thou - sand years or more I'll praise His name.
CHORUS
C F/C C7 Bb/F F
Ten thou - sand years we'll just be start - ed;
Dm Dm7 G7 C7sus
Ten thou - sand years we've just be - gun;
C7 Bb/F F A7/E Dm F9/C
The bat - tle's o - ver and the vic - t'ry's been won,
Bb Bbm6 F Gm7 C7 F
Ten thou - sand years and we've just be - gun!

WE'RE TOGETHER AGAIN

Words and Music by GORDON JENSEN and WAYNE HILTON
Arr. by W. Elmo Mercer

C7
F7
First time only
B♭7
B♭
D
pres - ence fills the room, And right now I am ex -
Je - sus said He would do; When the Spir - it fell from
Heav - en, by and by; Oh, my, what re -
First time begin slow rhythm
E♭
D7
Gm
Gm
F
pect - ing some-thing spec-ial, some-thing more; We're to-geth-er a - gain,
Heav- en, oh, the joy it did af - ford; They were to-geth-er back then,
joic - ing! this time for-ev-er - more; We'll be to-geth-er a- gain,
C7
E♮
F7
B♭
(we're) prais-ing the Lord!
- prais-ing the Lord!
(and) prais-ing the Lord!
Chorus:
B♭
B♭7
We're to-geth-er a-gain prais - ing the Lord!

E♭
F7
We're to-geth-er a-gain
in one ac-cord;
B♭
Some - thing
good is gon - na hap - en, some - thing
B♭7
E♭
good is in store; We're to - geth - er a - gain,

C7
F7
1 - 2
B♭
prais-ing the Lord!
2. When God's
3. And some
3
B♭
(Lord!)
Gm
Gm7
We're to-geth-er a-gain,
C7
F7
B♭
B♭7
D
and prais - ing the Lord,
E♭
B♭
We're to-geth-er a-gain!
8va
8va

WHEN IT'S TIME

Words and Music by ROGER L. HORNE
Arr. by W. Elmo Mercer

With a country feel
Ab Db Ab Eb7 Ab Db Ab
1. We have
Ab Ab7
heard a - bout His com - ing for so long, We have
years we've seen the scrip - tures all ful - filled, And we're
Db Ab Cm/Eb Eb7
heard it preached and heard it told through song; And, tho' I
wait - ing now for Je - sus to ap - pear; Soon the
Ab C C7 Fm Db
do not know the time, still I know this for sure: He'll re -
saints of all the a - ges will join the song of vic - to - ry, Prais - ing
Ab Bbm Db/Eb Eb7 Ab Db/Ab Ab
turn a - gain for me some glo - rious day!
Je - sus will be our end - less theme!

CHORUS
Ab Db Db/C Bbm Bbm7
When it's time, He will come; Then we'll
When it's time, He will come,
Eb7 Ab A°7 Eb7sus/Bb Eb7 Db/Eb Ab
know the bat-tle's been won; We will lay our ar- mor
Then we'll know
Ab7 Ebm7 Db Bb7 Ab Db
down, and pick up our robe and crown, Then we'll go home to be with
Ab/Eb Eb7 1. Ab Db/Ab Ab D.S. 2. Ab Db/Ab Ab
Je - sus, when it's time! 2. Thro' the time!

THANK GOD, I AM FREE

Words and Music by JAMES McFALL

CHORUS

F Bb
Thank God, I am free, free, free from this world of
F C7
sin: Wash'd in the blood of Je - sus, been born a -
F F
gain; Hal - le - lu - jah, I'm saved, saved, saved
Bb F Bb
By His won - der - ful grace; I'm so glad that I
F C7 F Bb F
found out He would bring me out and show me the way.

HOSANNA

Words and Music by TIM SHEPPARD
Arr. by Jon Sherberg

Gmaj7 A/G F♯m7 Bm7 Em7 A7sus4 A7 G/D D G/D
— my — sin, — Yes, I be - lieve — in love. —
— in — space — have need of a - ny - thing? —
9
D E D A/C♯ G D/F♯ G G/F♯ Em7 A7sus4 A7
Love has — tri - umphed; death — is — fin - ished. I can - not — con - cieve —
Yet my — soul — shall — ne - ver — cease — to — of - fer — gifts — of — praise. —
Dadd9 D F♯sus4 F♯ Bm A F♯m7 Gmaj7 A/G F♯m7 Bm7
— Why One so love - ly, — One — so — kind — would
— I kneel in spi - rit — at — His — feet, — A
17
Em7 Asus4 A7 G/D D A
give new — life — to — me.
sin - ner — saved — by — grace.
Born to die — to rise —

G D A G A Bm
— a - gain — To crush the pow'r— of Sa - tan's— sin. — I —
A G D C G
lift my— voice; I'll — shout — and — sing. — Ho - san - na!— Ho -
25
D A C G D
san - na! — Ho - san - na to — the King. —
C G Bm Bm F♯7/A Bm C♯o Bm

F♯7/A♯ D/A B/G Gmaj7 D/F♯ Em7 A7sus4 A7
1. G/D D
2. G/D D Bm Dmaj7/A Gmaj7 A/G F♯m7 Bm7
Lit - tle ba - by in a man - ger, Yes,
Em7 A7sus4 A7
37
D G/D D
I be - lieve in love.
D/C Cadd9 D/C Gadd9/B G A7 F♯m/A Gmaj7 Em/G Dsus7 D
rit.
8va
rit.
Ped.

I FEEL GOOD

Words and Music by LANNY AND MARIETTA WOLFE

Arranged by W. Elmo Mercer

Last time to
Eb7/G Ab6 Eb/Bb Bb7
1 & 4
Eb Eb7/G Ab Eb/Bb
I've been re-deemed makes me feel good! I feel
2 & 3
Eb Eb7/G Ab Eb/Bb
VERSE
Eb Ab/Bb
good!
1. Oh, how well do I re -
2. Now I'm on my way to
3. Oh, when my trav - 'ling days are
Eb7 Eb7/G Ab Eb
mem - ber all the days I spent in sin, With no
Heav - en and I'm sing - ing as I go, I'm so
o - ver and I reach that hap - py place, Ev - 'ry -
Eb Bb7 Fm7
tho't of do - ing all the things I should;
glad my name is writ - ten in the Book;
thing up there will be just like it should;

B♭7
E♭
E♭7
E♭7/G
But then the bless - ed Sav - ior found me and He
Just to know His blood has cleansed me and I'm
And when I step in - side the cit - y and I
A♭
E♭/B♭
E♭7/G
A♭6
gent - ly took me in; Makes me want - a shout, "Hal - le -
read - y now to go; Makes me want - a shout, "Hal - le -
see my Je - sus' face, I'm a - gon - na shout, "Hal - le -
E♭/B♭
B♭7
E♭
E♭7/G
A♭
E♭/B♭
NC
CODA
D.S.
E♭
lu - jah! I feel good!"
lu - jah! I feel good!" I feel good!
lu - jah! I feel good!"
E♭7/G
A♭
rit.
E♭
I feel good! I feel good!

MAN CAN'T LIVE BY BREAD ALONE

Words by GLORIA GAITHER

Music by WILLIAM J. GAITHER

G7
C7
3rd time to Coda
home – Man needs some - thing more than
F
C7(sus)
Verse
F
bread.
1. Fine pos -
2. There's a
B♭/F
C7/F
F
ses - sions nev - er quench the thirst - ing,
full - ness in the love of Je - sus,
B♭
C
Wealth just leaves man lean and poor;
Fills the emp - ti - ness we feel

C7
C9
F
B♭
Rich - es, for - tune,
'Til we no - tice
C7
Dm
Dm7
G9
mf
lux - u - ry, a - bun - dance –
man - na all a - round us –
Still man
Each new
mf
Gm7
C7
D.S.
cries: "There must be more!"
day a brand new meal.
Coda
F
B♭
F
F
Fine
bread, some - thing more than bread.
rit.

NOW I BELONG TO HIM

Words and Music by R. DOUGLAS LITTLE
Arr. by W. Elmo Mercer

CHORUS
Gm7 G 9(+11) F F/C C
He loved me when I was un - wor - thy; His
G7 G7 F/A G/B C Gm7 G 9(+11) F
blood paid the debt of my sin; My all is sur -
F/C C C/G C#° Dm7 1-2. G13 G7
ren - dered to Je - sus, Now I be - long to
C rall. G7(sus) G13 3. G13 rit. G7 C
Him! long to Him!
rall.
rit.

IT'S MY DESIRE

Words and Music by JIMMY PEARCE
Arr. by W. Elmo Mercer

Bb/F F7 Eb/F F7 1. Bb Eb/F 2. Bb
sire ___ to live for Him. 2. It's my de - Him.
sire ___ to live for
(Bb) Cm7 Bb/D Eb Eb/Bb Bb
If you could see where Je - sus bro't me from, To where I am to -
Bb6 Dm/A Gm Gm(maj7) Gm7 C9 C13 C7 Eb6/F F7 Eb/F F7
day, You would know the rea - son why I love Him so; ___ Now you can
Bb Fm7 Bb9 Bb7+ Eb6 Ab7
take the world's wealth and rich - es, I don't need earth's fame; It's my de -
Eb/F Ab9 (Repeat twice) Bb/F Eb/F F7 Gb Ab9 Bb
sire, ___, it's my de - sire ___ to live for Him! ___

SOMEONE IS PRAYING FOR YOU

Words and Music by LANNY WOLFE
Arranged by W. Elmo Mercer

(G) Gmaj7 G7 C
hope, some-one's pray - ing for you this ver - y
cares, and He knows_ just how much _ you can
Am7 D7
day, And "Peace, be still!" is al - read - y on the
bear; He'll speak your name _ to some - one in
G C/D CHORUS Parts G Gmaj7 G7
way. Some - one is
pray'r.
C G
pray - ing for you;

Em Em(maj7) Em7 A7(+11) A13 Am7
Some - one is pray - ing for you;
D7 G7 C
So when it seems you're all a - lone, And your
B B7/D♯ Em G/D
heart would break in two, Re - mem - ber, some - one is
D7 1 G C/D 2 G
pray - ing for you. 2. When it you.
8va

SWEET SURRENDER

Words and Music by STEPHEN R. ADAMS
Arr. by W. Elmo Mercer

C Cmaj7 C6 C Db Dbmaj7
Db6 Db C
1. No more strug-gling, no more try-ing, no more
2. No more heap-ing_ my hopes up high___ and feel-ing re-
Dm
wor- ry - ing o-ver fool-ish plans;___
sent - ment if they don't come true;___
Just the calm and the
No more the vic-tim of my
Dm G7 C
sweet as - sur-ance that my life is in His hands;___
sit - u - a - tion but re - ly-ing on what the Lord can do;

C F A7
Fac-ing now in one di - rec-tion, leav-ing all that I've loved be -
Say - ing thanks for giv - ing me Him-self and know-ing He is all I
Dm G7
hind; Mak - ing ev - 'ry mo-ment a sweet, com-plete sur-
need; Mak - ing of my prob-lems a sweet, com-plete sur-
C F/G
ren - der.
ren - der.
Chorus:
C Dm7
Sweet,
C7/E F Dm7
sweet sur - ren - der;

G7
C
Sweet, sweet surrender;
Dm7(sus)
G7
C
C7
Sweet, sweet surrender;
F
D7
G7
F/G
G7
Surrender to the will of
1 C
F/G
God.
2 C
God.
8va

STAND BY THE RIVER

Words and Music by DOTTIE RAMBO
Arr. by David Huntsinger

B♭
1. The road's been long, I'm a lit - tle bit ___ wea - ry;
2. You paved a road through the hills ___ and the moun - tains;
B♭7
E♭
Lot a miles ___ be - hind me, But home's ___ a lot
In the mid - dle of the des - ert You placed a
B♭
B♭7
near - er. I got one more ___ cross - ing; It's a long way
foun - tain. ___ Now stand by me, Je - sus, through the cold, deep
E♭
B♭
F7
B♭
o - ver. ___
wa - ter. ___
Won't You stand by the riv - er, wait for me. ___

CHORUS
F7 B♭
Won't You stand by the riv - er, Hold my trem-ble - in'
F7
hand. Cra - dle me, sweet Je - sus, from the cold,
B♭ B♭
dark, sink - in' sand. This is one trip I can't
B♭7/D E♭ G♭7
take a - lone; I'm get-tin' anx-ious to make it home.
B♭ F7 B♭
Stand by the riv - er, wait for me.

THE SWEETEST WORDS HE EVER SAID
(I Forgive)

Words and Music by JOEL HEMPHILL

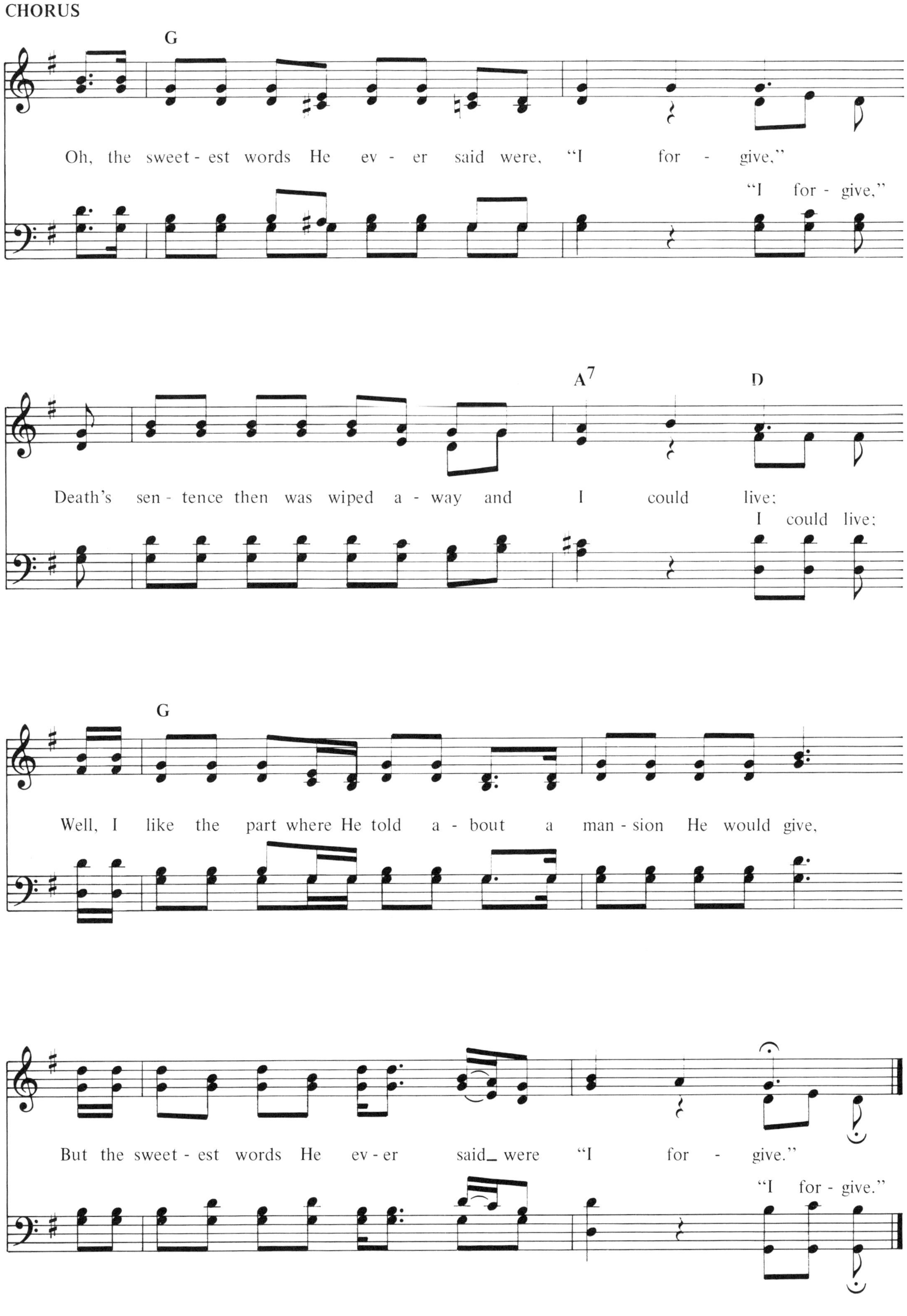
CHORUS
G
Oh, the sweet - est words He ev - er said were, "I for - give,"
"I for - give,"
A7
D
Death's sen - tence then was wiped a - way and I could live;
I could live;
G
Well, I like the part where He told a - bout a man - sion He would give,
But the sweet - est words He ev - er said_ were "I for - give."
"I for - give."

THIS IS JUST WHAT HEAVEN MEANS TO ME

Arr. by W. Elmo Mercer

C G7 C F C
Oh,
Now } this is just what heav-en means to me!
For
CHORUS
C F C
What joy 'twill be when we get o-ver yon - der, And
F/C C A+ A7 D7 G7 C
join the throng a - round the crys - tal sea! To meet our loved ones
F C C G7
and crown Christ for - ev - er, Oh, this is just what Heav-en means to
1,2. C F C D.S.
me!
3. C rit. F Fm6/D C FINE
me, means to me!

BRING ALL YOUR NEEDS TO THE ALTAR

Words and Music by DOTTIE RAMBO

Introduction
B♭
B♭7
E♭
F7
B♭
B♭
D♭°
Cm7
F7
1. Walk bold - ly to stand in His pres - ence; ___ Lay
2. He watch - es the fall of the spar - row, ___ Con -
B♭
claim to the prom - ise He made. ___ Your
cerned with the lil - ies so fair. ___ How
B♭7
E♭
soul can be cleansed 'neath the flow of the foun - tain; His
much more He cares for the sheep of His pas - ture! So

F7
Bb
blood wash - es guilt all a - way.
bring Him your bur - dens to bear.
Chorus
Bb
Db
Cm7
F7
Bring all your needs to the al - tar,
Bb
Bring all your needs to the Lord.
Bb7
Eb
He is so will - ing and a - ble to help you;
F7
Bb
D.S.
Bring all your needs to the Lord.

IF I HAD IT TO DO ALL OVER AGAIN

Words and Music by DALLAS HOLM
Arranged by W. Elmo Mercer

If I
G
Am
C
D7
Am/D
G
C/G
had it to do all o-ver a-gain I'd serve Je-sus ev-'ry day of my life, For I've
looking-ing for life, Stop look-ing right now, for it's Je-sus that can give life to you, So just
found He a-lone can real-ly sat-is-fy and de-liv-er me from all sin and strife. Yes, it's
o-pen your heart and un-lock it's door, and let Jesus cleanse your life thro' and thro'.

Chorus
C G D7 C G
Je - sus, the on - ly one, Je - sus, God's on-ly Son, Yes, it's
C G Am7 D7 1 G C
Jc - sus that set my soul free, and it's Jesus Christ that's coming back for me.
G C/G 2 G G C/G G
So if you're me. So, if I had it to do all
Am C D7 Am/D G C G C/G G
o-ver a-gain, I'd serve Je-sus ev-'ry day of my life.

JESUS
(HE MEANS ALL THE WORLD TO ME)

Words and Music by LANNY WOLFE
Arranged by W. Elmo Mercer

B♭ B° F/C F/E♭ D7
Pil - low__ for a wea - ry brow, a Shel - ter from the cold,
Shep - herd ____ whose love brings a stray back to the fold,
Gm F/A Gm/B♭ F/C C♯° Dm D7 Gm7 Am/C C7 F B♭/C B♭6/C
Je - sus is all of these, and more, to ____ my soul!
Je - sus is all of these, and more, to ____ my soul!
CHORUS
Parts
F F9 F♯9 G9
Je - sus, Je - sus, He means
Gm C+ Gm7 Am/C E/C F B♭/C B♭6/C
all ____ the world to me; ____

F F9 F#9 G9
Je - sus, Je - sus, With -
Gm D+ Gm7 C9 Am/C C7 1. F Bb/C
out Him, where would I be? 2. He's a
2. A+ A7 C/D Co/D Cm6/D
be? With - out
rit. Gm D7+/A Bb C9 Am/C C7 F Fmaj7 Bb/F F
Je - sus, where would I be?
rit.

LOVE LETTERS

Words and Music by DOTTIE RAMBO
Arr. by David Huntsinger

Moderately (not too fast)

smoothly
C
C Dm7 C7/E
1. I was going through mem-'ries and treas-ures to-day; —
(2.) count-ed the gifts You had giv-en so free. You
(3.) light of a can-dle I picked up my pen. —
(4.) just read Your an-swer with tears in my eyes; The
F
F Em7 Dm7
Found Your Love Let-ters I'd hid-den a-way. There was
nev-er stopped giv-ing with no word from me. They were
Words don't come eas-y — How do I be-gin? Oh I
stage has been set for the Groom and the bride. But I
C
C G/B Am7
ten-der e-mo-tion with each stroke of Your pen. I
wrapped in silk rib-bons with notes marked in red. I
pray I've not wait-ed too long to re-ply. —
shud-der to think just how sad life would be If

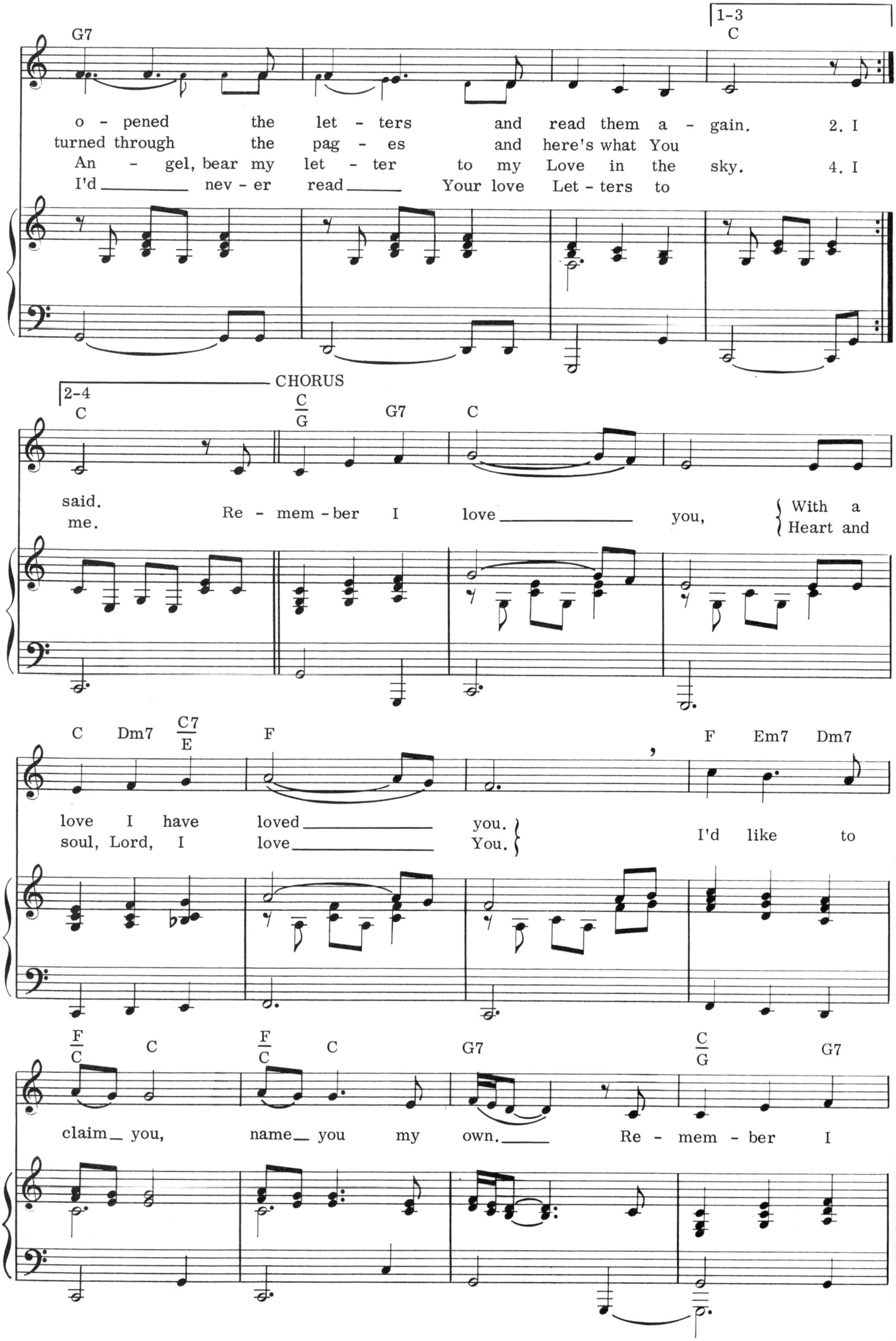
1-3
G7
C
o - pened the let - ters and read them a - gain. 2. I
turned through the pag - es and here's what You
An - gel, bear my let - ter to my Love in the sky. 4. I
I'd never read Your love Let - ters to
2-4
CHORUS
C
C/G
G7
said.
me.
Re - mem - ber I love you,
With a
Heart and
C Dm7 C7/E F F Em7 Dm7
love I have loved you.
soul, Lord, I love You.
I'd like to
F/C C F/C C G7 C/G G7
claim you, name you my own. Re - mem - ber I

C
C Dm7 C7/E
F
love you, With a love I have loved you.
Heart and soul, Lord, I love You.
When you
F Em7 Dm7
C
G7
Last time to ⊕
doubt that I do, Count the tears scat-tered through my Love Let-ters to
C
Fm6
G7sus
G7
D.S. al CODA
you.
3. By the
⊕ CODA
C
Fm6
C
Fm6
C
Fine
you.

I WILL PRAISE HIM

Words by GLORIA GAITHER

THOMPSON

Music by JOHN W. THOMPSON

Am
Em/G
F
C/E
Sweet com-mun - nion — I hard-ly know_
F
F/G
C
Am
Em/G
where He stops and I be - gin.
Sweet ___ free - dom — there's
F
A♭
C/G
F/G
F(add2)/G
G7
no price too high; It's been worth it all ___ to know I'm clean with - in.
I will
C
F(sus2)/C
F/C
C
Am
C/G
F
Em7
mf
praise Him know - ing that my praise will cost me ev - 'ry -
mf

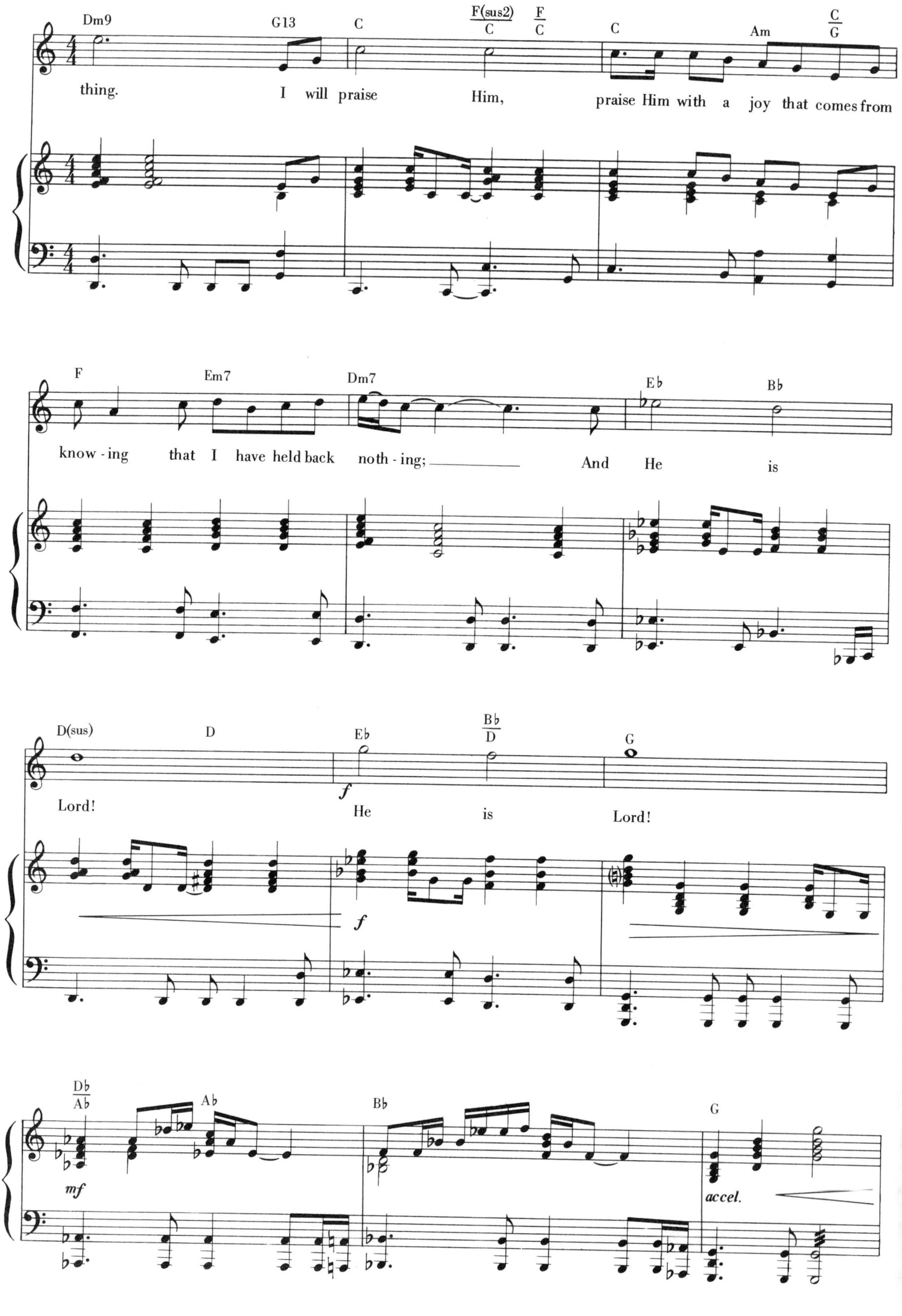
Dm9 G13 C F(sus2)/C F/C C Am C/G
thing. I will praise Him, praise Him with a joy that comes from
F Em7 Dm7 Eb Bb
know - ing that I have held back noth - ing; And He is
D(sus) D Eb Bb/D G
Lord! He is Lord!
f
Db/Ab Ab Bb G
mf
accel.

*Sing whole note "C" on "Lord" on 1st and 2nd repeats only.

I CAME ON BUSINESS FOR THE KING

Words and Music by JOEL HEMPHILL

F
Bb
1. Some - one here needs help and I can't do much,
2. Let's not hur - ry through and close up our hearts,
C
But if we keep on prais - ing He'll send His touch;
With pro - grams so well planned, we leave out His part;
F
Bb
F
Heal - ing for bod - y and soul He will bring,
Let's pause for a mo - ment, to His Spir - it to cling,
C7
F
I came on bus - 'ness for the King.

CHORUS

I came on bus - 'ness for the King,
He told me to smile and He told me to sing;
C
F
Bb
F
I can't just stand here and do my own thing,
C7
F
I came on bus - 'ness for the King.

I'M GONNA BE GONE

Words and Music by LANNY AND MARIETTA WOLFE
Arranged by W. Elmo Mercer

C#o
G/D
E7
A7
D7
Last time to
I'm gon-na be gone, and it won't be long, I'm gon-na be gone!
G
G7/B
C
G/D
Tacit
VERSE
G
Gon-na be gone!
1. This old world's not get-ting bet-ter, Ev-'ry day it's get-ting worse, So much
2. It could be just an-y morn-ing, It could be at night or noon; We don't
A7
D7
C
G
fight-ing and con-fu-sion go-ing on down here on earth; But
know just when He's com-ing, but we know He's com-ing soon! I can

(G)
A7
I don't let it both - er me, 'Cause I'm not here to stay;
say with calm as - sur - ance this old world is not my home;
D7
I know my Lord is com-ing soon, and
One of these days you're gon - na look for me, Praise
C
G
Tacit
I'll be caught a - way!
God, I'm gon - na be gone!
I'm gon - na be gone
CODA
G
G7
B
C
G
D
D
no rit.
G
(gone).
Gon - na be gone!
no rit.

I'M SOMEBODY BECAUSE I'M GOD'S CHILD

Words and Music by JOHN STALLINGS
Arr. by W. Elmo Mercer

Bb/C C7 F A+ A7
ry; The Lord knows I did not de -
I know that we shall be
not appear what we shall be;. . . . . But when He appears we shall be
Bbmaj7 Bb Gm7 C7 Bb/C C7
serve it, But He saved an old sin - ner like
like Him, Oo
like Him. . . . What a thrill!. . . . . What a thrill when His face we shall see!
F6 F+/B♮ CHORUS Bb
me.
There was noth - ing with - in me to
Bb F/A Gm7 F F/E Dm A+ Dm Dm7
mer - it God's love; There were none of His bless - ings I was

G7 C7 A7+ A7
wor - thy of; And when Sa - tan re - minds me, I
Gm/B♭ F/A Gm F/A Gm/B♭ F/C Dm
say with a smile: I'm not God's child be -
F/C D7 D7(♭9) Gm C9 (no 3rd) Am/C C7/E
cause I'm some - bod - y, I'm some - bod - y be - cause I'm God's
1
F C9 (no 3rd) Am/C C7 B♭/F F
child! Oo cause I'm God's child!
2
8
3

I KNOW HIS NAME

Words and Music by JIMMY PEARCE
Arr. by W. Elmo Mercer

F7
Gm
Gm7
C7
B♭/C
F
And all that life can mean be-cause I know Your name.
Cm7
E♭/F
F7(♭9)
B♭
Gm7
Am7
Hav - ing found the joy I'd long been search - ing for,
D9
Gm(sus)
Gm
Gm
C9
C13
Fmaj 7
I find I wast - ed much the life I lived be-fore;
Cm7
E♭/F
F7(♭9)
B♭
B♭+
Gm
B♭/C
Am7
But now for You I'll live, and not for world - ly fame

D9 Gm(sus) Gm C9 Bb/C F
I'll nev - er be the same be-cause I know Your name.
Cm7 Bb/F F7(b9) Bb Gm Gm7 C7 Am7
And now for Him I'll live, and not for world - ly
D9 Gm Gm7 C7 Bb/C C7
fame; I'll nev - er, nev - er be the same, Be - cause I
Bb/F F rit. Bb/F F
know His name, I know His name.
rit.
8

SEEKING FOR ME

Words and Music by LANNY WOLFE
Arr. by W. Elmo Mercer

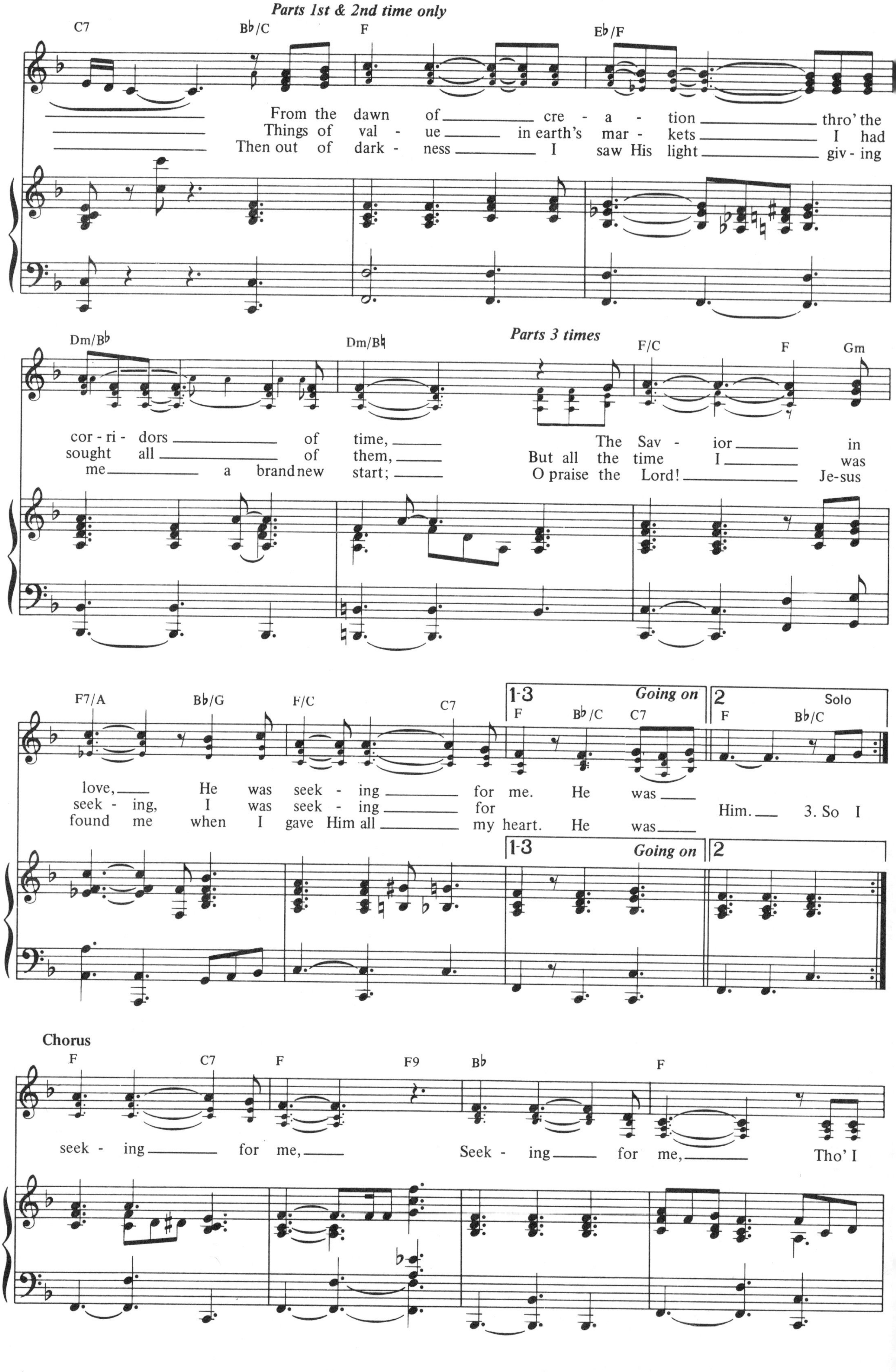
Parts 1st & 2nd time only
C7 Bb/C F Eb/F
From the dawn of cre - a - tion thro' the
Things of val - ue in earth's mar - kets I had
Then out of dark - ness I saw His light giv - ing
Dm/Bb Dm/B♮ Parts 3 times F/C F Gm
cor - ri - dors of time, The Sav - ior in
sought all of them, But all the time I was
me a brand new start; O praise the Lord! Je - sus
F7/A Bb/G F/C C7
1-3 Going on
F Bb/C C7
2 Solo
F Bb/C
love, He was seek - ing for me. He was
seek - ing, I was seek - ing for Him. 3. So I
found me when I gave Him all my heart. He was
1-3 Going on
2
Chorus
F C7 F F9 Bb F
seek - ing for me, Seek - ing for me, Tho' I

F Am/E Dm G7 C7 B♭/C C7
knew Him not still He loved me and was seek - ing for me. He was
F C7 F F7 F7/A B♭ B°7
seek - ing for me, Je-sus was seek - ing for me; Tho' I
F/C F Gm F7/A B♭/G F/C C7
knew Him not still He loved me and was seek - ing for
1 Solo 2
F F9/A B♭ B♭/C F F9/A B♭ B♭/C F
me! 2. He was me!

JESUS, THE RESURRECTION

Words and Music by RICH COOK
Arr. by W. Elmo Mercer

VERSE
G C/G G7 C C7 Gm7 C7 F F#o C/G C
1. Sin was my mas - ter with death as wag - es,
2. Tho' I was dead I now am liv - ing,
G7 G7 Dm7 G7 C G7 C7
Caught in the clutch - es of guilt and shame;
I am a - live in Je - sus' name;
3
F F#o C/G E7/B Am Am7 D9
Then Je - sus came and loosed my shack - les, No more
His death at Cal - v'ry re - placed my suf - f'ring, I'm res - ur -
D7 Am7 D7 G Am7/G G7 D. S. C rit. F/C C
sin could free - ly reign. life!
rect - ed to sing His praise!
8
rit.

NOBODY ELSE BUT JESUS

Words and Music by JIMMY PEARCE

Chorus

Ab Ab+ Fm/Ab Bb9 Ab/Eb Eb Ab/Eb Eb7
no-bod-y else — but Je - sus could set my spir-it free;
(spir-it free —)
mf
Ab Ab+ Fm/Ab Bb9 Ab/Eb Eb Fm7 Bb7
No-bod-y else — but Je - sus could share my mis - er - y. —
Eb Gm7 Abmaj7 Fm7
No-bod-y else — could take — my place — up - on Mount Cal - va - ry; —
Eb/G Ab Eb/Bb C7(-9) Fm7 Bb7 Eb
1
No-bod-y else — but Je - sus could do that much for me. —
Ab/Bb D.S.
2
Fm7 Ab/Bb Bb7 Eb Db9 Eb Fine
do that much for me.

LET ME FEEL YOUR SPIRIT ONCE AGAIN

Words and Music by JOEL HEMPHILL

B♭ E♭ B♭
1. Lord, I've been bus - y here and there,
2. I re - mem - ber vic - t'ry in my soul,
C7 F
Till life's bur - dens and its plea - sures have crowd - ed out my prayer;
And the close, sweet fel - low - ship we shared made joy - ful riv - ers flow;
B♭ E♭
But now I find I'm emp - ty, and if I con - fess my sin,
And though I've been ne - glect - ful, Lord, You know where I've been,
Cm F7 B♭
Would You let me feel Your Spir - it once a - gain.
And I need to feel Your Spir - it once a - gain.

CHORUS
F7
Bb
Lord, I need to feel Your pow - er___ and the joy in my soul.
C7
F
F7
And the sweet peace that on - ly comes when Je - sus has con - trol;___
Bb
Eb
I don't want to walk this road;_ I know where it ends,
Cm
F7
Bb
Would You let me feel Your Spir - it___ once a - gain.___

IT MADE NEWS IN HEAVEN
(When I Got Saved)

Words and Music by GORDON JENSEN

D G D
1. It did-n't make the pa-pers_ in this world when I prayed through,
2. Not long a - go a beg-gar,_ now a child_ of the King,
(D) E7 A
It did - n't seem to mat - ter_ to all, but just a few;_
This old world just shrugged it's shoul - ders,_ it did - n't mean a thing;_
A7 D G
But in the gold - en streets of glo - ry,_ cel - e - bra - tion ban - ners waved;
But_ it was God's ap - pro - val,_ _my spir - it real - ly craved;
(G) G/D D Em D/F A7 D
It made news in Heav - en, when I got saved!

CHORUS

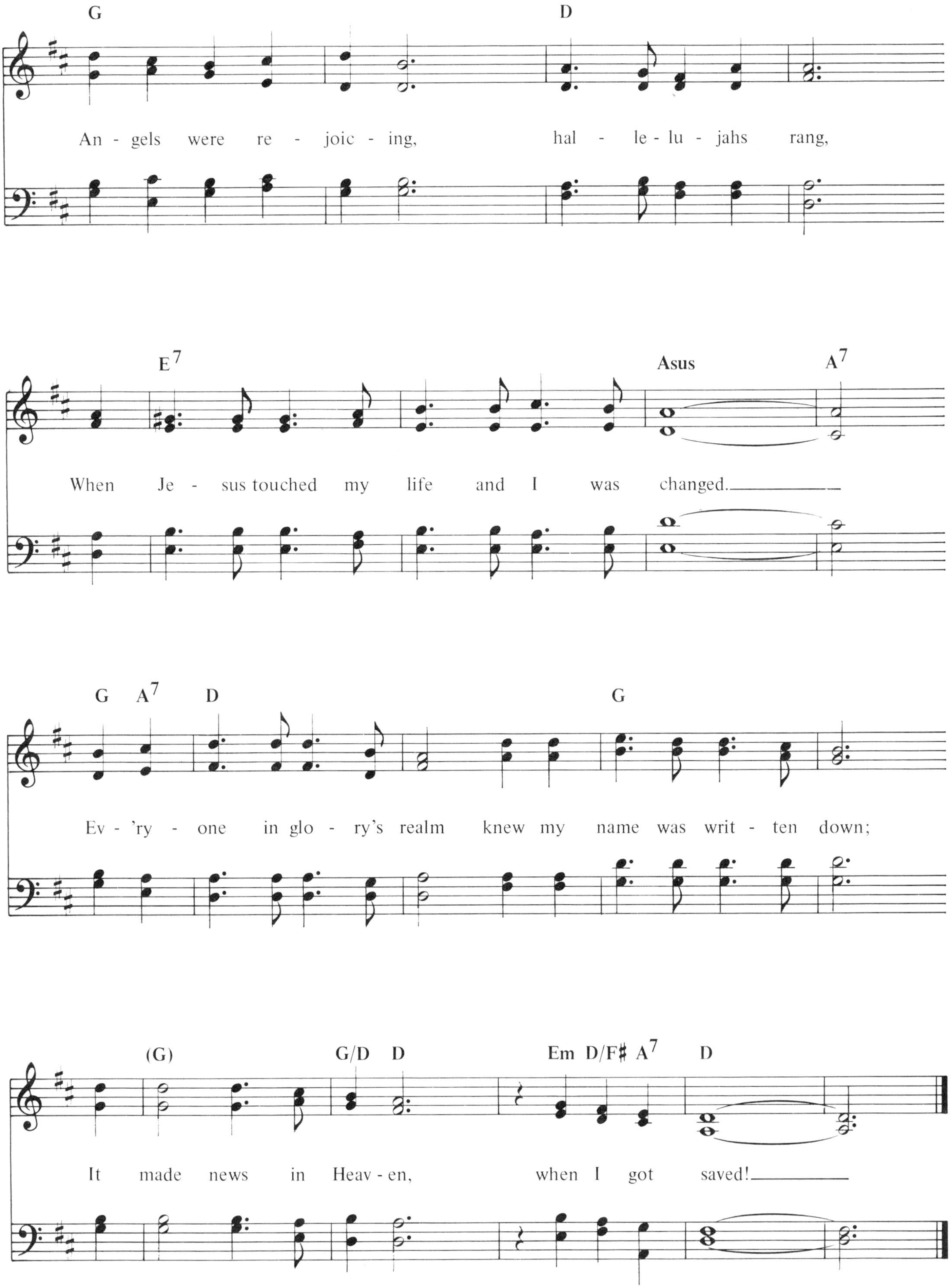
G D
An - gels were re - joic - ing, hal - le - lu - jahs rang,
E7 Asus A7
When Je - sus touched my life and I was changed.
G A7 D G
Ev - 'ry - one in glo - ry's realm knew my name was writ - ten down;
(G) G/D D Em D/F♯ A7 D
It made news in Heav - en, when I got saved!

THE HOLY HILLS OF HEAVEN CALL ME

Words and Music by DOTTIE RAMBO

C G7 C
1. The ho - ly hills of heav - en call me, To man - sions
2. I see loved ones o - ver yon - der, Tears are
G C F
bright a - cross the sea; Where loved ones wait and crowns are
gone and hearts are free; And from the throne my Sav - ior
C F C G7 C
giv - en; The hills of home keep call - ing me.
beck - ons, And the hills of home keep call - ing me.
CHORUS
G7 F G7 C G7
This house of flesh is but a pri - son, Bars of

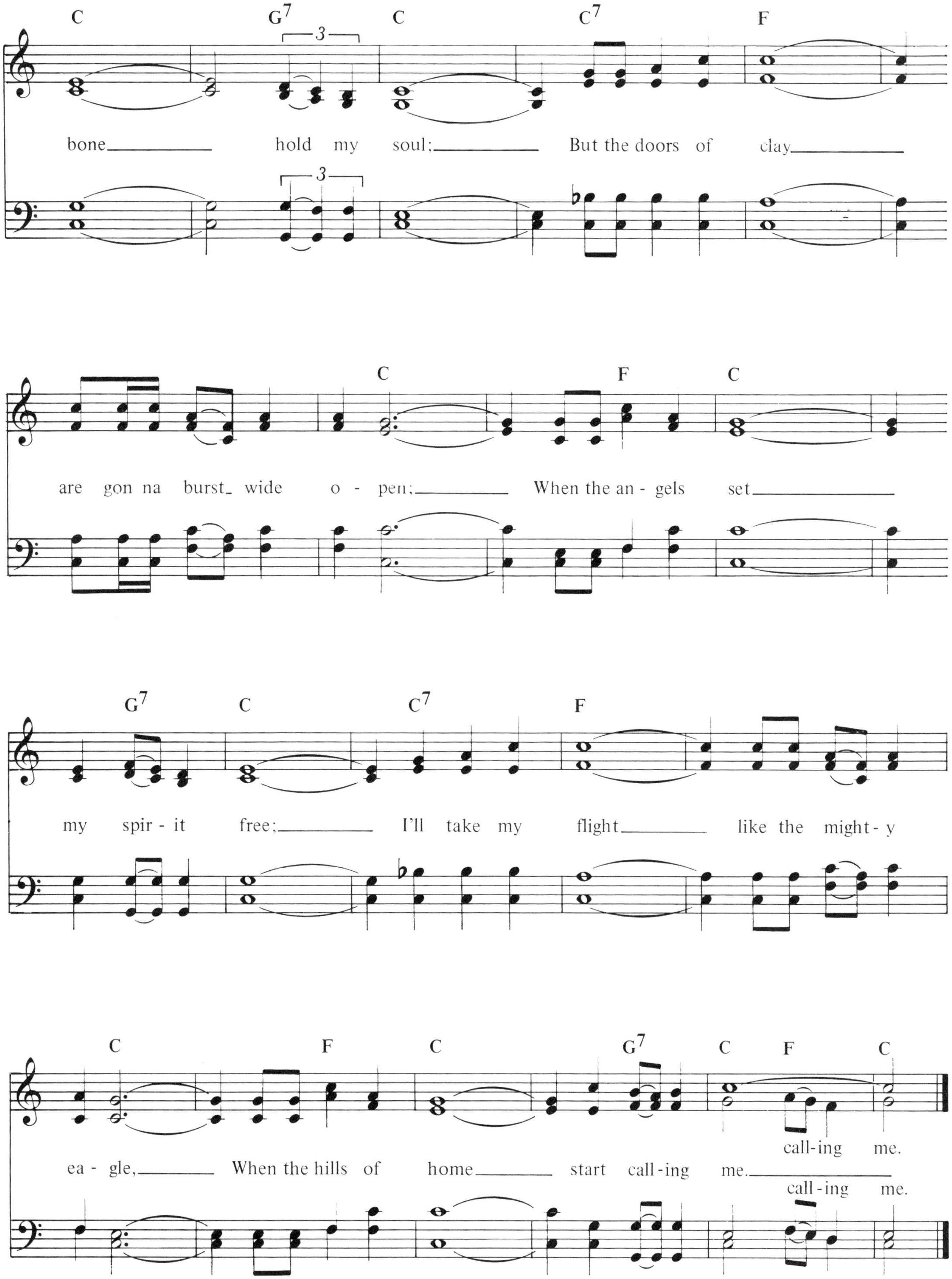
C G7 C C7 F
bone hold my soul; But the doors of clay
are gon na burst wide o - pen; When the an - gels set
C F C
G7 C C7 F
my spir - it free; I'll take my flight like the might - y
C F C G7 C F C
ea - gle, When the hills of home start call-ing me.
call-ing me.
call - ing me.

THE WIND IS BLOWIN' AGAIN

Words and Music by LANNY WOLFE
Arr. by W. Elmo Mercer

C
G
— they came to see what it was all a - bout; — There was a
— as the proph-et Jo - el said it would do; — For Pe - ter
(G)
Em
A7
sound that came down from the up - per — room, - where the Ho - ly Ghost was
said on the day of — Pen - te - cost, - it's for you and your
D7
G
be - ing poured out; — It sound - ed just like the roar of a
chil - dren, — too; — So, o - pen up your heart and let the

G/B C C7 B7+ Bb13 A7
might-y wind, As it fell on ev-'ry one of them, And the
wind blow in, You'll nev-er, nev-er be the same a-gain, For the
G/D B7/D# Em A7(b9) C/D
wind that blew at Pen-te-cost, Praise God, it's blow-in' a-gain!
wind that blew at Pen-te-cost Keeps blow-in' and blow-in' a-gain!
D. S. twice
G G7/B C C/D
The
CODA
G F/G F#/G G
It's blow-in' a-gain!
opt. repeat and fade
D. S. twice
CODA
opt. repeat and fade

THERE'S JUST SOMETHING ABOUT MY JESUS

Words and Music by TERRY HARPER
Arr. by W. Elmo Mercer

Cm
E♭7/B♭
Fm
B♭7
see There's some-thing a-bout my Je - sus,
Last time to ⊕
Fm7
B♭7
A♭/B♭
E♭
VERSE
E♭
E♭(add9)
Some-thing a-bout the Lord.
1. When at the first some-one came and
2. Now it's a great big won-der-ful
C7
F7
F7/C
F7
told me a-bout this Je - sus, the Naz-a - rene, Said He'd
feel-in', now that I'm walk-in' with my new-found Friend, His
B♭7
Fm/B♭
Gm/B♭
E♭
E°7
be ev-'ry-thing an-y - one could ev - er need;
love just keeps get-tin' bet-ter ev - 'ry day;

Fm Bb7 Eb Eb(add9) C7
Well, I real - ly didn't be - lieve it,
And you'll nev-er know this joy I'm feel - in'
F7 F7/C F7
un-til I met Him for my - self, And now I
un-til you find Him for your - self, And when you
Bb7 Fm/Bb Gm/Bb Bb7 Eb Eb/G Ab
know just what they real - ly mean.
find Him you'll just have to say:
Eb/Bb Ab/Bb Bb7
There's just
CODA
Eb Ab Eb
(Lord)

HE RESTORETH MY SOUL

Words and Music by DOTTIE RAMBO

INTRO.

G C G D7 G D7 G
1. When I'm low in spir - it I cry, "Lord, lift me up;
2. It's dark as a dun - geon and the sun sel - dom shines,
G7 C G
I___ want to go high - er with Thee."___
And I ques - tion,"Lord, why must this be?"___
C G G7 C
But the Lord knows I can't live on the moun - tain,___
But He tells me there's strength in my sor - row,___

D D7 G
So He picked out a val - ley for me.
And there's vic - t'ry in tri - als for me.
CHORUS
G C G D7 G G7
He leads me be - side still wa - ters,
still wa - ters,
C D G
Some where in the val - ley be - low.
G7-9 C F7
He draws me a - side to be tes - ted and tried,
G D7 G
But in the val - ley He re - stor - eth my soul.

I JUST LOVE LOVIN' THE LORD

Words and Music by RICH COOK

F C7 F7 B♭
that's why they sing, But that a - lone, my friend, is not e -
B♭m/G B♭m/A B♭m F F7/E♭ D7
nough for me be-cause I just love lov - in' the Lord more than
Gm Gm/C C7 2nd time to ⊕ F F7 B♭7 F B♭/C
an - y - thing else that I do! Do you
F F7 B♭7
go to church to see a friend and to find out the news of the week?
F B♭/C F
Do you go to hear the choir sing or to

G7 C7 F
hear the preach-er preach?_ The preach-in', the sing - in'
Gm/C F C7 F7 Bb
and the fel - low - ship sweet,_ But that a - lone, my friend, is not e -
Bbm/G Bbm/A Bbm F F7/Eb
nough for__ me___ be-cause I just love lov - in' the Lord_
D7 Gm Gm/C C7 F F7 Bb7
more than an - y - thing else_ in the world!
CODA
F F F7 Bb7 F
world!

IS THERE ANYTHING I CAN DO FOR YOU?

Words and Music by DOTTIE RAMBO
and DAVID HUNTSINGER

I'VE NEVER BEEN THIS HOMESICK BEFORE

Words and Music by DOTTIE RAMBO

Country (with a ♪. ♬ feel)
Introduction
D A7 D
D
1. There's a light in the win - dow, the ta - ble's spread in splen - dor;
2. I can see the fam - 'ly gath - er, sweet fa - ces all fa - mil - iar;
G D
Some - one's stand - ing by the o - pen door. I can
No one's old or fee - ble an - y - more. This
G D D7 G
see a crys - tal riv - er So I must be near for - ev - er.
lone - some heart is cry - ing; Think I'll spread my wings for fly - ing. Lord, I've

D A7 D
nev - er been this home - sick be - fore.
Chorus
D D7 G
See the bright Light shine, It's just a - bout home time. I can
D A7
see my Fa - ther stand - ing at the door. This world's been a
D D7 G D
wil - der - ness, I'm read - y for de - liv - er - ance. Lord, I've nev - er been this
A7
1
D
2
D
home - sick be - fore. fore.

IF I COULD SING A THOUSAND MELODIES

Words by W. ELMO MERCER
and JOHN T. BENSON, JR.

Music by W. ELMO MERCER

INTRO.
8va
Bb
Eb
Gdim
1. If I could sing a thou-sand mel - o - dies,
2. If I could sing like one great sym-pho - ny,
Bb
F
Bb
I'd sing and nev - er cease, How great my God!
My God would ev - er be, My on - ly song
Eb
Gdim
I'd sing of love, His wis - dom, might and pow'r,
My voice would break, All bar - ri - ers of sound

B♭ F7 B♭
Each day and pass - ing hour, I'd sing of Him.
To sweep the world a-round, I'd sing of Him.
REFRAIN
B♭ E♭ B♭ E♭ B♭
I'd climb some moun-tain high, I'd sing in - to the sky, 'Til heav'n and
C7 F7 B♭
earth would hear my song; If I could sing a thou-sand
E♭ Gdim B♭ F7 B♭
mel-o-dies, I'd sing and nev-er cease, How great my God!

I WANT TO THANK YOU, JESUS

Words, Music and Arr. by JANE AND DON MARSH

Boldly
ff
Bb
Bb/Ab
GmaddC Gm
GmaddC Gm
Ab
Bb/Ab
Eb/G
mf
rubato
8va
Bb
Bb7
Cm/Bb
1. For the way You took my sins, I want to thank You;
(2. For the) way You changed my life, I want to thank You;
Cm
F9sus
Dm/F
F7
Cm/Bb Bb
For the way that You for-give, I want to praise You.
For the peace on-ly You can give, I want to praise You.

Bbmaj9 Bb9sus Bb13 Bb9
And if I had a mil-lion years just to thank You, for the
Ebmaj7 Ebm/C f Bb/F
man-y ways that You have shown Your love to me, I would just be-
F9sus Dm/F F9sus F7 rit. triplet feeling Bbadd9 Bb
gin, for I owe so much to You.
sim.
rit.
triplet feeling
Bbadd9 Bb Bb Eb
I want to thank You, Je - sus, I want to

C F
thank You, Je - sus, I want to
D Gm
thank You Je - sus, I want to
Cm7 Dm Eb F9sus F7
give You the praise. You gave Your
Bb Bb7 Eb
life to save me, And now You

C
C7
F
3
live with - in me. I want to
3
3
D
D7
Gm
1
Cm7
Dm/F
F7
thank You, Je - sus, for all You mean to
3
3
Bb
Even 8ths
2
Cm
me. 2. For the all, for
F9sus
3
F13
F7
Bb
all You mean to me.
3
3

TEARS WILL NEVER STAIN THE STREETS OF THAT CITY

Words and Music by DOTTIE RAMBO

CHORUS
A♭ D♭ A♭
But
And tears will nev - er stain the streets of that ci - ty,
And
E♭7
No wreaths of death on my man - sion door:
A♭ D♭ A♭
Tear drops aren't wel - come be - yond the gates of glo - ry,
E♭7 A♭
'Cause the heart will nev - er break an - y - more.

THANK YOU, LORD

Words and Music by ROGER L. HORNE

F Am F7 Bb
1. Thank You, Lord, thank You, Lord, thank You for the val - leys,
2. There've been times when my heart would seem like it was break - ing,
3. Day by day, week by week, year by year, I need Him,
Bbm F Gm C7 Bb6 Bb
For when I reach the moun-tain high I'll see where You have led me;
I had no - one ex - cept the Lord to stop the pain, and ach - ing;
This life's too cruel to face a - lone, I've learned to trust up - on Him;
F Am F7 Bb
I'll look up - on the storm - y way And see the past be - hind me,
In dark - est hours I've gone to Him, He's clos - er than a broth-er,
And when it comes my time to leave, Oh, please don't weep my part - ing,
Bbm F Gm C13 C7 Bb6 Bb F
I'll know 'twas best I go this way, the way that led to vic - t'ry.
He gives me strength to car - ry on, a - bove Him there's no oth - er.
A life of joy, all trials be - hind, in Heav'n I'll just be start - ing.

CHORUS
F7(4) F7 Bb Bb+ Gm/Bb C7 C9 F6 F F7(4) F7
Let come what may to-day, to-mor-row, Lord, I'm hold-ing on to You, I'll do what-
Bb Bb+ Gm/Bb C7 C9 F6 F C7sus C7
e'er You ask for I could ne'er re-pay You for all You've done for me; There are
F Am F7 F13 F7 Bb
bat-tles yet that I must fight, there'll be prob-lems, may-be sor-row, but I
Bbm F
know You've gone this way be-fore,
1.-2.
Gm C13 C7 Bb6 Bb F
so thank You, Lord, thank You.
3.
Gm/Bb Am Bb G°7/Bb F
Thank You, Thank You, Thank You, Lord,

I'LL SEE YOU IN THE RAPTURE

Words and Music by CHARLES B. FELTNER

Bb Bb7 Eb
1. If we nev - er meet a - gain on this earth, my pre - cious friend,
2 To my loved ones let me say that there'll sure - ly come a day
Bb Bb7 Eb
If, to God, we have been true and we've lived a - bove all sin,
When the Lord will come a - gain and He'll take His bride a - way;
Ab Fm7 Bb7 Eb
Then, for us, there'll be a greet - ing, for there's gon - na be a meet - ing,
So, get read - y now to meet Him, and with hal - le - lu - jahs greet Him,
Ab Bb7 Eb
I'll see you in the rap - ture some sweet day.

CHORUS
Eb Ab Bb7 Eb
I'll see you in the rap - ture, see you in the rap - ture,
Ab Bb7 Eb
See you at that meet - ing in the air;
Ab Bb7 Eb
There, with our bless - ed Sav - ior, we'll live and reign for - ev - er,
Ab Bb7 Eb
I'll see you in the rap - ture some sweet day.

I WILL GLORY IN THE CROSS

Words and Music by DOTTIE RAMBO

G/D D7 G
will - ing to die in my place.
love made pro - vi - sion for me.
CHORUS
G C/G G G7/B
I will glo - ry in the cross, in the cross. Lest His
C Bm7 Am7 G
suf - f'ring all be in vain. I will
G G7/B C Cm
weep no more for the cross that He bore; I will
G/D Bm/D D7 1. G 2. G
glo - ry in the cross. cross.

I OWE IT ALL TO THEE

Words and Music by ROGER L. HORNE
Arranged by W. Elmo Mercer

Am/C E7/B Am G/D D7 G C G
G D7 G7 C Cm6 G
1. A life that was use - less He found crum - bled in sin,
val - ues were twist - ed, I played life's fool - ish game,
D7 Bm/E F♯ G
Fight - ing a bat - tle I nev - er could win; Then
Think - ing that to - mor - row my luck had to change! But to -
(G) G7 C F9
lay - ing the ru - ins of my life at His cross turned out to
mor - rows have come and to - mor - rows have gone, and I've found

D/G D7 G (G) C/A G7/B
be my great - est gain, not my loss. (Ah)
out life's one sure thing is Christ the Lord! (Ah)
CHORUS
C G
All that I am, or ev - er hope to be,
D7 D9 G Gmaj7 G7
I owe it all to Thee;
C G Am/C E7/B Am
All that I have You have giv - en me, I owe it
G/D D7 1. G C/G G 2. G
all to Thee! 2. My Thee!
D.S.

IS THAT THE OLD SHIP OF ZION?

Words and Music by CONRAD COOK